Great Jewish Quiz Book

The Great Jewish Quiz Book

Barbara Spector

The Jewish Publication Society
Philadelphia · New York · Jerusalem
5746 · 1986

Manufactured in the United States of America
Library of Congress Cataloging in Publication Data
Spector, Barbara.
    The great Jewish quiz book.
    Bibliography: p. 157
    1. Jews—Miscellanea.   2. Judaism—Miscellanea.
DS102.95.S64   1986   909'.04924   85–23797
ISBN 0–8276–0259–6
    0–8276–0260–X (pbk.)

Designed by Adrianne Onderdonk Dudden

*This book is dedicated
to the memory of my father,*
LEON SPECTOR
1918–1981

Acknowledgments

A very special thank you to my editor, David A. Adler, who had the initial idea for this book and encouraged me to write it.

Other people deserving kudos for their encouragement, talent, assistance—and patience—are:

Adrianne Onderdonk Dudden, my friend and one of publishing's top designers, for giving this book its distinctive appearance.

Linda R. Turner, whose valuable assistance and moral support helped make production progress smoothly.

Carol Flechner, Dennis Dolan, and Jim Leonard for their sharp eyes and improvements to my manuscript.

The staff of The Jewish Publication Society and the Executive Vice President, Nathan Barnett, for their enthusiasm and support.

Mr. Mitchell Panzer, member of the Board of Trustees of The Jewish Publication Society, for volunteering his time to act as a consultant.

Steven Blitz and Sidney Goldschmidt for their contributions of questions to the Purim and Chanukah quizzes.

David Saltzberg and Louis Forgione of Waldman Graphics, Inc.; Roxanne McAllister of The Book Press; and Donna Bell and Fred Klinger of The Lehigh Press, Inc., for turning my typewritten manuscript into a typeset, printed, bound book.

Everyone who let me use his or her photo in the "Guess Who?" quiz.

All the friends and relatives who put up with me while I was researching and writing—especially my mother, Shirley Spector, and my brother, Kenneth Spector.

Without the support of all these wonderful people, there would be no book.

Contents

1. What was the name of the first computer at the Weizmann Research Institute in Rehovot, Israel?
    (a) Shalom I;   (b) Rosh I;   (c) Dybbuk I;   (d) Golem I.

2. Who was the first Jewish Miss America?
    (a) Golda Myerson;   (b) Bess Myerson;   (c) Phyllis George;   (d) Belle Silverman.

3. Jacob Barsimson was the first Jew to _____.
    (a) swim the English Channel;   (b) arrive in New Amsterdam;   (c) serve on the Supreme Court;   (d) attend Harvard University.

4. In what year did a Jew first receive the Nobel Prize?
    (a) 1921;   (b) 1915;   (c) 1905;   (d) 1910.

5. Who is considered the first Jew?

6. Who was the first woman to serve on a Supreme Court?

7. The first Jewish-American citizen was _____.
    (a) Asser Levy;   (b) Haym Salomon;   (c) Judah Touro;   (d) Rebecca Gratz.

8. In what year did Israel's first supermarket open?
    (a) 1948;   (b) 1951;   (c) 1953;   (d) 1958.

Answers on page 18

9. According to the Talmud, Rabbi Akiva was the first one to use which expression?
(a) *"L'chaim!"*;   (b) *"Mazel tov"*;   (c) *"Kayn aynhoreh."*

10. Who was the first *kohen*?

11. Luis de Torres, a Jew, was the first member of Columbus's crew to set foot in America. He was also the first white man known to participate in what Indian ritual?

12. Which Jew was the first millionaire in America?
(a) Haym Salomon;   (b) Harmon Hendricks;   (c) Judah Benjamin;   (d) Levi Strauss.

13. In eighteenth-century Virginia a Portuguese-Jewish physician, Dr. Siccary, introduced which plant to the United States?
(a) the carrot;   (b) the tomato;   (c) the palm tree;   (d) the petunia.

14. Al Jolson, the star of the first "talkie," was Jewish. What was his father's occupation?
(a) a rabbi;   (b) a cantor;   (c) a Hebrew school teacher;   (d) a jazz singer.

15. Who was the first Sephardic Jew to win the Nobel Prize?
(a) Menachem Begin;   (b) Saul Bellow;   (c) Murray Gell-Mann;   (d) Baruj Benacerraf.

16. Who was the first American woman to receive a Nobel Prize in science?
(a) Sally Jane Priesand; (b) Judith Kaplan Eisenstein; (c) Sandy Eisenberg Sasso; (d) Rosalyn S. Yalow.

17. Judith A. Resnik, killed in the tragic space shuttle explosion of January 28, 1986, was the
(a) first American woman in space; (b) second American woman in space; (c) first American Jew in space.

18. Lillian D. Wald (1867–1940), who founded the school-nurse program, turned the back yard of the Henry Street Settlement on New York's Lower East Side into the first _____.

19. Which Jewish custom was introduced by Chaim Nachman Bialik?
(a) the *oneg Shabbat*; (b) exchanging *shalach manot* on Purim; (c) planting trees in Israel; (d) breaking a glass at weddings.

20. Who was Israel's first Sephardic president?

1. Which Old West figure had a Jewish wife?
   (a) Jesse James;   (b) Butch Cassidy;   (c) Wyatt Earp;   (d) Wild Bill Hickok.

2. When Bess Myerson entered the Miss America competition in 1945, the pageant sponsors wanted her to do something. She refused. What was it?

3. Which one of the following Jews never appeared on a U.S. postage stamp?
   (a) Samuel Gompers;   (b) Albert Einstein;   (c) George Gershwin;   (d) Henry Kissinger.

4. Over what eye did Moshe Dayan wear his eye patch?

5. What is the better-known name of Israeli statesman David Gruen?

6. Which one of the following heroes of the Holocaust period was not Jewish?
   (a) Mordecai Anilewicz;   (b) Anne Frank;   (c) Hannah Szenes;   (d) Raoul Wallenberg.

7. How did Anne Frank begin each entry in her diary?
   (a) "Dear Diary";   (b) "Dear Kitty";   (c) "Dear Friend."

Answers on page 18

8. The main street of Tel Aviv is named after Meir Dizengoff. Who was he?
   (a) the first mayor of Tel Aviv;   (b) the first president of Israel;   (c) a philanthropist who donated money to Israel;   (d) the first Sephardic chief rabbi of Israel.

9. Who is known as the "father of modern Hebrew"?
   (a) Noah Webster;   (b) Eliezer Ben-Yehuda;   (c) Theodor Herzl;   (d) David Ben-Gurion.

10. Which one of the following Jews has never won a Nobel Prize?
    (a) Henry Kissinger;   (b) Menachem Begin;   (c) Golda Meir;   (d) Albert Einstein.

11. This Dutch artist lived for more than twenty years in Amsterdam's Jewish quarter and used his Jewish neighbors as models.
    (a) Jan Vermeer;   (b) Rembrandt Harmenszoon van Rijn;   (c) Vincent van Gogh;   (d) Jan Steen.

12. Who was known as the Prince of Commentators?
    (a) Rashi;   (b) Rambam;   (c) Moses;   (d) Mike Wallace.

13. Who wrote and illustrated *Chicken Soup with Rice*?

14. Which one of these famous Isaacs is not Jewish?
(**a**) Isaac Bashevis Singer;   (**b**) Isaac Asimov;   (**c**) Sir Isaac Newton;   (**d**) Isaac Stern.

15. Where was Haym Salomon born?
(**a**) England;   (**b**) Poland;   (**c**) Philadelphia;   (**d**) Lithuania.

16. Which one of the following people was not a product of New York's Lower East Side?
(**a**) Senator Jacob Javits;   (**b**) Irving Berlin;   (**c**) Albert Einstein.

17. American poet Emma Lazarus did not become interested in her Jewish background until she visited _____.
(**a**) Jerusalem;   (**b**) Congregation Shearith Israel;   (**c**) Ellis Island;   (**d**) Russia.

18. In what U.S. city did young Golda Meir live?

19. When Albert Einstein was a boy, his father feared that Albert was _____.
(**a**) in poor health;   (**b**) skipping Hebrew school;   (**c**) mentally deficient;
(**d**) wasting too much money.

20. What was Groucho Marx's real first name?

1. Which one of these famous boxers was not Jewish?
   (a) Mushy Callahan;   (b) Leach Cross;   (c) Frankie Madden;   (d) Al McCoy.

2. How many gold medals did swimmer Mark Spitz win in the 1972 Olympics?

3. Which Jewish player was baseball's first designated hitter?

4. Which of the three horse races in the Triple Crown is named after a Jew?

5. Where is the Jewish Sports Hall of Fame located?

6. In what year was Israel first represented in the Olympics?

7. Which one of these former National Hockey League players is not Jewish?
   (a) Mike Veisor;   (b) Larry Zeidel;   (c) Bernie Wolf;   (d) Bernie Parent.

8. Which Jewish athlete was known as "Mr. Basketball"?

9. How tall was Barney Sedran, one of the greatest of the early professional basketball players and a member of the Basketball Hall of Fame?
   (a) 5′11″;   (b) 5′7″;   (c) 5′4″;   (d) 5′2″.

Answers on page 18

10. Which one of the following Jewish athletes was a weightlifter?
(a) Barry Asher; (b) Ike Berger; (c) Hank Wittenberg; (d) Dick Savitt.

11. In what year were the first Maccabiah Games held?
(a) 1917; (b) 1932; (c) 1949; (d) 1968.

12. In what sport did Sidney Franklin, a Jewish athlete from Brooklyn, compete in Spain?

13. At which university did former quarterback Benny Friedman coach football?
(a) Hebrew University; (b) Brandeis University; (c) Penn State University;
(d) Notre Dame University.

14. John M. Brunswick (1819–1886), a Jew, built the first perfect _____ in the U.S.
(a) billiard table; (b) basketball net; (c) pogo stick; (d) swimming pool.

15. Which Jewish athlete is known as the first great T-formation quarterback and is in the Football Hall of Fame?

16. How many of the "Wonder Five," the great basketball team of the Catholic St. John's University in 1931, were Jewish?

17. True or false: Mark Spitz has never competed in the Maccabiah Games.

18. In what sport does Jewish athlete Nancy Lieberman compete?

19. Joe Jacobs, the manager of boxer Max Schmeling, is often quoted ("We wuz robbed" and "I should have stood in bed"). What was Jacobs's nickname?
   (**a**) "The Little Hebrew";   (**b**) "The Pride of the Ghetto";   (**c**) "Yussel the Muscle"; (**d**) "The Bronx Beauty."

20. Max Baer, the great boxer of the 1930s, wore a Star of David on his boxing trunks. How many of his four grandparents were Jewish?

Jewish "Firsts" Answers

1. (d) Golem I. 2. (b) Bess Myerson. 3. (b) arrive in New Amsterdam. 4. (c) 1905 (Adolf von Baeyer, for chemistry). 5. Abraham. 6. Miriam Ben-Porat of Israel was the first female member of any Supreme Court in the world. She was appointed in 1977. 7. (a) Asser Levy. 8. (d) 1958 (September, in Tel Aviv). 9. (a) *"L'chaim!"* 10. Aaron. 11. Smoking a peace pipe. 12. (b) Harmon Hendricks (a Sephardic Jew who founded America's first copper-rolling mill in the late 1700s). 13. (b) the tomato. 14. (b) a cantor. 15. (d) Baruj Benacerraf (1980, medicine and physiology). 16. (d) Rosalyn S. Yalow. 17. (b) second American woman in space and (c) first American Jew in space. 18. City playground. 19. (a) the *oneg Shabbat*. 20. Yitzhak Navon.

Answers

People, People, People Answers

1. (c) Wyatt Earp. 2. Change her name (to Meredith or Merrick). 3. (d) Henry Kissinger. 4. The left eye. 5. David Ben-Gurion. 6. (d) Raoul Wallenberg. 7. (b) "Dear Kitty." 8. (a) the first mayor of Tel Aviv. 9. (b) Eliezer Ben-Yehuda. 10. (c) Golda Meir. 11. (b) Rembrandt Harmenszoon van Rijn. 12. (a) Rashi. 13. Maurice Sendak. 14. (c) Sir Isaac Newton. 15. (b) Poland. 16. (c) Albert Einstein. 17. (c) Ellis Island. 18. Milwaukee. 19. (c) mentally deficient. 20. Julius.

Jews in Sports Answers

1. (c) Frankie Madden. (The real name of Mushy Callahan was Vicente Morris Scheer; Leach Cross was actually Dr. Louis C. Wallach; and the real name of Al McCoy was Al Rudolph.) 2. Seven. 3. Ron Blomberg. 4. The Belmont Stakes (after August Belmont, Sr., the banker who was the first president of the American Jockey Club and the leading U.S. horse breeder of the nineteenth century). 5. In Netanya, Israel. 6. 1952. 7. (d) Bernie Parent. 8. Nat Holman. 9. (c) 5'4". 10. (b) Ike Berger. 11. (b) 1932. 12. Bullfighting. 13. (b) Brandeis University. 14. (a) billiard table. 15. Sid Luckman. 16. Four (Max Posnack, Max Kinsbrunner, Albert "Allie" Schuckman, and Jack "Rip" Gerson). 17. False. 18. Basketball. 19. (c) "Yussel the Muscle." 20. He had one Jewish grandfather.

1. Rosh Hashanah and Yom Kippur take place in the Hebrew month of Tishri. What's Tishri's zodiac sign?

(a) the scorpion;   (b) the lion;   (c) the scales;   (d) the goat.

2. True or false: Rosh Hashanah falls on the first day of the first Hebrew month.

3. How many days of Rosh Hashanah are celebrated in Israel?

4. Why aren't pickles served at Rosh Hashanah dinner?

5. The prayer book for the High Holidays has a special name. What is it?

6. True or false: Rosh Hashanah can never fall on a Sunday.

7. Why is round challah eaten on Rosh Hashanah?

8. What does a *ba'al tekiah* do in the synagogue on the High Holidays?

9. On the afternoon of the first day of Rosh Hashanah, in a ceremony called *tashlich*, it is customary to go to a flowing body of water and symbolically cast one's sins away. In this ceremony what is thrown in the water to symbolize our sins?

(a) coins;   (b) bread crumbs;   (c) a chicken;   (d) stones.

Answers on page 34

10. The word *shofar* comes from the Hebrew root that means _____.
     (a) hollowness;   (b) horn;   (c) judgment.

11. The ancient Jews sounded the *shofar* on all but one of the following occasions. Which one is the exception?
     (a) to announce the new moon;   (b) to announce a bar mitzvah;   (c) to lead their armies into battle;   (d) to announce the king.

12. How many Days of Awe are there?
     (a) eight;   (b) seven;   (c) ten;   (d) forty.

13. At the height of the 1934 pennant race, one baseball player refused to go on the field on Yom Kippur. Who was he?

14. Which fruit is cut up and dipped in honey to symbolize our hope for a sweet year?

15. In some synagogues on Yom Kippur the ark is draped with a special curtain. What color is the curtain?

16. The prayer *Kol Nidre* releases a Jew from which of the following?
     (a) wrongs committed against other people;   (b) vows made to God;   (c) oaths sworn in court;   (d) all of the above.

17. In the *kapparah* ceremony, performed on the day before Yom Kippur, what is circled over the head three times?

  (**a**) rope;   (**b**) a *shofar*;   (**c**) a rooster;   (**d**) a *tallit*.

18. If Yom Kippur falls on Shabbat, do we still fast?

19. The Hebrew word for "sin," *chet*, is also the word for _____ .

  (**a**) "evil";   (**b**) "lazy";   (**c**) "missing the target";   (**d**) "getting lost."

20. How many sins are mentioned in the prayer *Al Chet*?

  (**a**) 120;   (**b**) 70;   (**c**) 44;   (**d**) 22.

The people whose photos appear on this quiz all have famous faces. However, in these photos they are much less recognizable (because they are shown as youngsters, without make-up, or in an uncharacteristic setting). How many of them do you know?

1. The twelve-year-old in this photo later became world-renowned as the "father of psychoanalysis."

2. The military chaplain shown in this photo is an ordained rabbi, a former editor of The Jewish Publication Society, and the author of *The Chosen*.

Answers on page 34

3. The young man swinging the bat later pitched for the Los Angeles Dodgers.

4. This three-year-old grew up to write the score for the musical *West Side Story* and the motion picture *On the Waterfront.*

5. This young woman, shown
here at age sixteen, later became
the founder of Hadassah.

6. The young woman playing the Statue
of Liberty in this youth-group pageant later
became the ruler of another country.

7. The little boy shown in this photo developed the Theory of Relativity.

8. This young man, shown with his sister Pauline, became the founder of political Zionism.

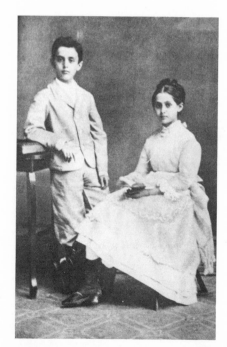

9. The woman shown holding her dog is a comedienne and former talk-show host.

10. The man in this photo is a frequent contributor of Yiddish stories to the *Forward* and the author of *Gimpel the Fool* and *Shosha*.

11. Which two Marx Brothers are shown as young men in this photo?
(**a**) Chico and Harpo; (**b**) Groucho and Chico; (**c**) Zeppo and Groucho;
(**d**) Groucho and Harpo.

1. Which one of these songs was *not* written by a Jew?
   (a) "Easter Parade";   (b) "Oklahoma";   (c) "Swanee";   (d) "Happy Birthday."

2. Which song was introduced as a wordless melody, had lyrics later written by a student in a Hebrew class, and now represents Jewish music to people everywhere?

3. A Jew, Irving Berlin (born Israel Baline), wrote the most popular Christmas song of all time. What is it?

4. In the Yiddish-theater adaptation of Shakespeare's *Hamlet*, Hamlet was a
   (a) factory owner;   (b) writer;   (c) banker;   (d) yeshiva student.

5. Is Chelm a real city?

6. What change was made in the song "Hatikvah" before it became Israel's national anthem?
   (a) The title was changed;   (b) The tune was changed;   (c) Another verse was added;   (d) The last two lines were changed.

7. Which two colors are saluted in the Hebrew song "Kachol Ve-Lavan"?

8. How tall is K'tonton, the Jewish pixie?

Answers on page 34

9. What musical instruments did Joshua and his army use to topple the walls of Jericho?

10. The poet Yehoash (Solomon Bloomgarten) translated the Bible into which language?
    (a) English;   (b) Russian;   (c) Yiddish;   (d) Swahili.

11. On Simchat Torah during the first year of Nazi occupation in Antwerp, the Jews who were still left in the city heard the bells of the cathedral play the tune of
    (a) "Deutschland über Alles";   (b) "Hatikvah";   (c) "The Star-Spangled Banner"; (d) "Havah Nagilah."

12. Which instrument does Isaac Stern play?

13. Naphtali Herz Imber was the author of the lyrics to which popular Israeli song?

14. Yehudi Menuhin, Itzhak Perlman, and Pinchas Zukerman all play the same musical instrument. Which instrument?

15. Who was known as the "sweet singer of Israel"?

16. The musical *Fiddler on the Roof* is based on a story by _____.

17. *The Dybbuk*, the play about the soul of a dead person that enters a living person, was written by _____.

    (**a**) Isaac Bashevis Singer;   (**b**) I. L. Peretz;   (**c**) S. An-Ski;   (**d**) Mary Shelley.

18. Which Yiddish writer, born Solomon Rabinowitz, took his pen name to distinguish himself from his father, who loved Hebrew and despised Yiddish literature?

Music and Literature

30

19. According to legend, what made the *golem* come to life?

    (**a**) matzah;   (**b**) the letters of God's name;   (**c**) soil from the Holy Land;   (**d**) a Star of David.

20. What was the name of the matchmaker in the musical *Fiddler on the Roof*?

1. How many personal names are mentioned in the Bible?
   (a) 5,000;   (b) 2,800;   (c) 960;   (d) 520.

2. What is Abba Eban's real first name?
   (a) Avraham;   (b) Alexander;   (c) Aubrey;   (d) Ashley.

3. What is the real name of comedian Albert Brooks?
   (a) Albert Cohen;   (b) Albert Birnbaum;   (c) Albert Einstein;   (d) Albert Levy.

4. The name *Ben-Gurion* means _____.
   (a) "son of a star";   (b) "son of a gun";   (c) "son of a lion cub";   (d) "son of my people."

5. In the Torah, Abraham's name was changed from Abram. What was Sarah's name before it was changed?

6. Which name is not the name of a book of the Bible?
   (a) Samuel;   (b) Joel;   (c) Noah;   (d) Jeremiah.

7. True or false: All descendants of the priestly family have the last name *Cohen*.

**First
Names,
Last
Names,
Real
Names**

31

Answers on page 34

First
Names,
Last
Names,
Real
Names

32

8. Which of the following names does not mean "Levi"?
(a) Levyn; (b) LaVine; (c) Segal; (d) Katz.

9. The name *Moses* comes from which language?

10. If your last name is Cantarini or Voorsanger, your ancestors probably _____.
(a) were priests in the Holy Temple in Jerusalem; (b) came from Spain; (c) were carpenters; (d) were cantors.

11. Which of the following family names does *not* come from the name of a color?
(a) Schwartz; (b) Roth; (c) Weiss; (d) Weiner.

12. What is the better-known name of Goldie Mabovitz Myerson?

13. What was the first name of the "Abraham" of Abraham & Straus?

14. Samuel Goldwyn, the film producer who was one of the founders of MGM Studios, changed his last name. What was it originally?
(a) Goldberg; (b) Goldman; (c) Goldfish; (d) Feingold.

15. Asa Yoelson starred in *The Jazz Singer*, the first "talkie." What was his more famous name?

16. What is the more famous name of sports announcer Howard Cohen?

17. What is the better-known name of comedian and filmmaker Allen Konigsberg?

18. What is the better-known name of Moshe Segal, an artist famous for his work in stained glass?

19. What was the real name of Harry Houdini?
    (**a**) Ehrich Weiss;   (**b**) Leonard Rosenberg;   (**c**) Benjamin Kubelsky;   (**d**) Nathan Birnbaum.

20. Joan Molinsky is a comedienne known for her ribbing of Hollywood personalities. What is her more famous name?

Answers

Shanah Tovah Answers

1. (c) the scales. **2.** False. (It takes place on the first day of the seventh Hebrew month.) **3.** Two. **4.** To avoid starting the New Year with a sour taste. **5.** The *machzor*. **6.** True. Rosh Hashanah never falls on Sunday, Wednesday, or Friday. **7.** To symbolize a full year. **8.** He blows the *shofar*. **9.** (b) bread crumbs. **10.** (a) hollowness. **11.** (b) to announce a bar mitzvah. **12.** (c) ten. **13.** Hank Greenberg. **14.** Apples. **15.** White. **16.** (b) vows made to God. **17.** (c) a rooster. **18.** Yes. **19.** (c) "missing the target." **20.** (c) 44.

Guess Who? Answers

1. Sigmund Freud. **2.** Chaim Potok. **3.** Sandy Koufax. **4.** Leonard Bernstein. **5.** Henrietta Szold. **6.** Golda Meir. **7.** Albert Einstein. **8.** Theodor Herzl. **9.** Joan Rivers. **10.** Isaac Bashevis Singer. **11.** (d) Groucho and Harpo.

Music and Literature Answers

1. (d) "Happy Birthday." ("Easter Parade" was written by Irving Berlin, "Oklahoma" by Oscar Hammerstein II, and "Swanee" by George Gershwin. "Happy Birthday" was written by Mildred and Patty Hill.) **2.** "Havah Nagilah." **3.** "White Christmas." **4.** (d) yeshiva student. **5.** Yes. **6.** (d) The last two lines were changed. (The original lines were "To return to the land of our fathers / To the city where David dwelt." These were changed to "To be a free people in our land / The land of Zion and Jerusalem.") **7.** Blue and white (the colors of the Israeli flag). **8.** Exactly the size of a thumb. **9.** *Shofars* (ram's horns). **10.** (c) Yiddish. **11.** (b) "Hatikvah." **12.** The violin. **13.** "Hatikvah." **14.** The violin. **15.** King David. **16.** Sholem Aleichem. **17.** (c) S. An-Ski. **18.** Sholem Aleichem. **19.** (b) the letters of God's name. **20.** Yente.

First Names, Last Names, Real Names Answers

1. (b) 2,800. **2.** (c) Aubrey. **3.** (c) Albert Einstein. **4.** (c) "son of a lion cub." **5.** Sarai. **6.** (c) Noah. **7.** False. **8.** (d) Katz. **9.** Egyptian. **10.** (d) were cantors. **11.** (d) Weiner. **12.** Golda Meir. **13.** Abraham. (His name was Abraham Abraham.) **14.** (c) Goldfish. **15.** Al Jolson. **16.** Howard Cosell. **17.** Woody Allen. **18.** Marc Chagall. **19.** (a) Ehrich Weiss. **20.** Joan Rivers.

1. Could red snapper be served in a kosher restaurant?

2. Who wrote in her diary, "In spite of everything I still believe that people are good at heart"?

3. The terms *shel rosh* and *shel yad* refer to the two _____ .

4. Who is supposed to fast on the day before Passover?

5. Boris Pasternak won the Nobel Prize for _____ .
   (**a**) literature;   (**b**) chemistry;   (**c**) economics;   (**d**) medicine and physiology.

6. Families with the last name Strassberg originally came from _____ .
   (**a**) Poland;   (**b**) Germany;   (**c**) France;   (**d**) Vienna.

7. Which of the following is *not* a holiday greeting?
   (**a**) "*Mazel tov*";   (**b**) "*Chag sameach*";   (**c**) "*Gut yontif.*"

8. What is kept in the Shrine of the Book?

9. What makes the sound *chiri bim, chiri bam*?
   (**a**) an Israeli parakeet;   (**b**) a squeaky wheel;   (**c**) a *shofar*;   (**d**) a Hasidic Jew.

10. Which author wrote most of his early works in Polish, believing that Yiddish and Hebrew would soon die out?

(**a**) Sholem Aleichem; (**b**) Isaac Bashevis Singer; (**c**) I. L. Peretz; (**d**) Sholem Asch.

11. Los Angeles Dodgers Hall of Famer Sandy Koufax, former Miss America Bess Myerson, and Dr. Jonas Salk, discoverer of the polio vaccine, are all members of which Jewish organization?

(**a**) American Jewish Committee; (**b**) B'nai B'rith; (**c**) The Jewish Publication Society; (**d**) League for Yiddish.

12. Which biblical patriarch was noted for opening his tent to receive guests?

13. During the last period of his life, Chaim Nachman Bialik (1873–1934) lived in Tel Aviv on a street named _____.

(**a**) Bialik Street; (**b**) Dizengoff Street; (**c**) King George Street; (**d**) Allenby Street.

14. Some Jewish communities have a special *Bikkur Cholim* society. What do the members of this society do?

15. The founder of B'nai B'rith was _____.

(**a**) Henry Jones; (**b**) Henrietta Szold; (**c**) Isaac Mayer Wise; (**d**) Cyrus Adler.

16. Which women's Zionist organization is named after Queen Esther's Hebrew name in the Bible?

17. Which of the following was *not* developed by a Jew?
    (a) blue jeans;   (b) the drive-in gas station;   (c) life insurance.

18. What code name was used for Hitler in the Warsaw ghetto?
    (a) Schwartz;   (b) Berkowitz;   (c) Horowitz;   (d) Rabinowitz.

19. A Jewish woman who has a three-year-old child converts to Christianity. Is the child still considered Jewish under Jewish law?

20. The Jewish Anti-Defamation League is a division of _____.
    (a) the United Nations;   (b) B'nai B'rith;   (c) the Federation of Jewish Agencies;
    (d) the Jewish Defense League.

1. Who named the birds and animals of the world?

2. How many talking animals are mentioned in the Bible?

3. Which Nobel Prize–winning author wrote the children's book *Why Noah Chose the Dove*?

4. How many of each kind of fish did Noah take on the ark?

5. What kind of bird did Noah first send from the ark?

6. When Noah sent the dove from the ark, did she bring back an olive branch in her beak?

7. What animal did Abraham offer as a sacrifice instead of Isaac?

8. The last name *Ochs* means _____.
   (**a**) rooster;   (**b**) goose;   (**c**) ox;   (**d**) eagle.

9. In the story of the Exodus, when the Egyptians chased after the Israelites, what animals were the Egyptians using for transportation?

Answers on page 44

10. How long did Jonah stay inside the belly of the great fish?

11. How long was Daniel in the lions' den?
    (a) overnight;   (b) three days and three nights;   (c) seven days and seven nights.

12. A *shofar* can be made from the horn of all but one of these animals. Which animal has horns that cannot be used?
    (a) antelope;   (b) gazelle;   (c) Rocky Mountain goat;   (d) cow.

13. What animal is mentioned more than 150 times in the Bible and is associated with the tribe of Judah?

14. According to the prophet Zechariah, when the Messiah comes, he will be riding on a _____.
    (a) white horse;   (b) camel;   (c) donkey;   (d) unicorn.

15. What animal was covered with armor by the Syrians in their battle against the Maccabees?

16. Luis de Torres, who sailed on Columbus's ship, noticed a strange bird in the New World. In a letter to friends back home he described it, using the Hebrew word for peacock—*tukki*. Today this bird is associated with American celebrations. What do we now call it?

17. According to the Talmud, which creatures are immune to the effects of the evil eye?

18. How do traditional Jews take care of their pets during Passover?
    (a) the same way they always do, since the Passover laws don't apply to animals;
    (b) they "sell" them to non-Jews, who take care of the pets during the holiday;
    (c) they feed the pets a special Passover diet.

19. In the song "Chad Gad-Ya," sung at the seder, what does the ox do?
    (a) eats the kid;   (b) bites the cat;   (c) drinks the water;   (d) hits the dog.

20. What does the name *Deborah* mean?
    (a) sheep;   (b) mountain goat;   (c) bee;   (d) deer.

1. Which two of the Three Stooges were brothers?
   (a) Moe and Larry;   (b) Moe and Curly;   (c) Larry and Curly.

2. True or false: Mr. Spock and Captain Kirk of the TV series "Star Trek" are both played by Jewish actors.

3. Which of the following roles was *not* played by a Jew?
   (a) the Fonz;   (b) Columbo;   (c) Quincy;   (d) Rhoda Morgenstern.

4. True or false: David Lee Roth, former lead vocalist of the rock group Van Halen and now a solo performer, is Jewish.

5. How many Marx Brothers were there?

6. What major 1981 movie told the story of Harold Abrahams, one of the leading sprinters in English track history?

7. Who were the two Jewish cops on the TV show "Hill Street Blues"?

8. What two famous Hollywood personalities did Dr. Max Nussbaum, of Los Angeles's Temple Israel, convert to Judaism?

Answers on page 44

9. In what year did Israel begin television broadcasts?
   (a) 1941;   (b) 1953;   (c) 1959;   (d) 1966.

10. Which Jewish TV game-show host originally wanted to go to medical school in Canada?

11. Who is the French-Jewish mime who worked in the underground during the German occupation of France in World War II and helped to smuggle Jewish children into Switzerland?

12. Milton Berle, who later became "Mr. Television," the first variety-show host, started his performing career as part of a vaudeville team. Who was his partner in those early days?
    (a) George Jessel;   (b) Imogene Coca;   (c) Kitty Carlisle;   (d) his mother.

13. Which Jewish entertainer/comedian wrote a letter to Governor William W. Scranton of Pennsylvania saying, "If you contemplate campaigning in any more Jewish neighborhoods I suggest you learn how to pronounce 'mishmash' "?

14. What was the name of Rhoda Morgenstern's sister in the TV show "Rhoda"?

15. Which one of these stars did not act in the Yiddish theater?
    (a) Paul Muni;   (b) Edward G. Robinson;   (c) Herschel Bernardi;   (d) Barbra Streisand.

16. What was the occupation of Eddie Cantor's father?
    (a) doctor;   (b) lawyer;   (c) accountant;   (d) cantor.

17. Which actress played Golda Meir in the original cast of the Broadway play *Golda*?

18. Which singing group, composed of three sisters, popularized the Yiddish song "Bei Mir Bist Du Schein" in the late 1930s?

19. Which song, taken from a Hasidic melody, has been recorded by Richard Tucker, Harry Belafonte, and Sammy Davis, Jr.?

20. Eugene Silverstein has starred in the movies *Young Frankenstein*, *Blazing Saddles*, and *The Woman in Red*. What is his better-known name?

Mishmash I Answers

1. Yes. **2.** Anne Frank. **3.** *Tefillin*. **4.** First-born males. **5.** (a) literature. **6.** (c) France. **7.** (a) *"Mazel tov."* **8.** The Dead Sea Scrolls. **9.** (d) a Hasidic Jew. **10.** (c) I. L. Peretz. **11.** (b) B'nai B'rith. **12.** Abraham. **13.** (a) Bialik Street. **14.** Visit the sick. **15.** (a) Henry Jones. **16.** Hadassah. **17.** (c) life insurance. (Blue jeans were invented by Levi Strauss; the drive-in gas station was developed by Louis Blaustein and his son Jacob.) **18.** (c) Horowitz. **19.** Yes. **20.** (b) B'nai B'rith.

Animals, Animals, Animals Answers

1. Adam. **2.** Two (the serpent in the Garden of Eden and Balaam's talking ass). **3.** Isaac Bashevis Singer. **4.** None. (Fish can swim and didn't have to be saved.) **5.** A raven. **6.** No. (It was a leaf.) **7.** A ram. **8.** (c) ox. **9.** Horses (pulling chariots). **10.** Three days and three nights. **11.** (a) overnight. **12.** (d) cow (because that was the shape of the Golden Calf). **13.** The lion. **14.** (c) donkey. **15.** The elephant. **16.** Turkey. **17.** Fish (because they live beneath the surface of the water and cannot be seen [Ber. 20a]). **18.** (b) they "sell" them to non-Jews, who take care of the pets during the holiday or (c) they feed the pets a special Passover diet. **19.** (c) drinks the water. **20.** (c) bee.

Show Time Answers

1. (b) Moe and Curly—born Horwitz but changed later to Howard. (Shemp [Sam Horwitz] was another brother.) **2.** True (Leonard Nimoy and William Shatner). **3.** (d) Rhoda Morgenstern. **4.** True. (He was active in Jewish youth organizations before he became a star.) **5.** Five (Harpo, Groucho, Chico, Zeppo, and Gummo). **6.** *Chariots of Fire*. **7.** Henry Goldblume and Mick Belker. **8.** Elizabeth Taylor and Sammy Davis, Jr. **9.** (d) 1966 (April). **10.** Monty Hall. **11.** Marcel Marceau. **12.** (d) his mother. (The act was called "Milton and Mom.") **13.** Groucho Marx. **14.** Brenda. **15.** (d) Barbra Streisand. **16.** (d) cantor. **17.** Anne Bancroft. **18.** The Andrews Sisters. **19.** "Havah Nagilah." **20.** Gene Wilder.

1. Sukkot is one of the three pilgrim festivals. What are the other two?

2. Is it permitted to eat an *etrog* after the Sukkot holiday?

3. What color does an *etrog* turn when it withers and dries up?

4. What is always the last part of a *sukkah* to be put up?

5. Which of the following *cannot* be used to make the roof of a *sukkah*?
   (a) straw;   (b) cornstalks;   (c) animal skins;   (d) bamboo reeds.

6. Should you put a *mezuzah* on your *sukkah*?

7. What are the minimum dimensions of a *sukkah*?
   (a) 4′ × 4′;   (b) 10′ × 10′;   (c) 25′ × 25′.

8. The Bible says that we should live in *sukkot* to remember our ancestors. Which ancestors?
   (a) Adam and Eve;   (b) Abraham and his family;   (c) the Israelites after the Exodus from Egypt;   (d) the Maccabees.

9. True or false: A *sukkah* must have four walls to be kosher.

Answers on page 55

10. The *sechach* of a *sukkah* is its _____.

    (a) roof;   (b) eastern wall;   (c) western wall;   (d) floor.

11. True or false: It is possible to buy a ready-made *sukkah* that can be set up without tools.

12. According to tradition, seven *ushpizin*, or "guests," are invited into the *sukkah*: Abraham, Isaac, Jacob, Moses, Aaron, Joseph, and _____.

13. Which one of the four species is also known as a citron?

14. When the four species are used on Sukkot, the blessing that is said mentions only one of them. Which one?

15. When you recite the blessing over the four species, in what hand do you hold the *etrog*?

16. In which direction are the four species waved first?

17. According to one interpretation of the significance of the four species, the *lulav* resembles the spine, the myrtle leaves are shaped like the eye, the willow corresponds to the mouth, and the *etrog* has the shape of the _____.

18. Do we shake the *lulav* on Shabbat?

19. All but one of the following *etrogim* are unfit for use. Which is the exception?
(**a**) an *etrog* with a hole;   (**b**) an *etrog* that is peeled;   (**c**) an *etrog* that is round like a ball;   (**d**) an *etrog* requiring two hands to hold it.

20. Which one of the following is *not* another name for Sukkot?
(**a**) Z'man Simchatenu;   (**b**) Yom Ha-Zicharon;   (**c**) Chag Ha-Asif;   (**d**) He-Chag.

1. What is the "Borscht Belt"?

   (a) nickname for what waiters in New York's Lower East Side restaurants use to hold up their pants;   (b) nickname for the area of Jewish resort hotels in the Catskill Mountains;   (c) nickname for the famous left hook of boxer Mike Rossman, "the Jewish Bomber";   (d) German variation of the traditional borscht (beet soup) recipe.

2. What is *shuckling*?

   (a) harvesting;   (b) the Yiddish word for "laughing";   (c) swaying of the body during prayer;   (d) an Israeli folk dance.

3. What is a *maimuna*?

   (a) an Israeli dance step;   (b) the last name of a famous rabbi;   (c) a picnic held by Moroccan Jews the day after Passover;   (d) a synagogue artifact used by the Jews of Yemen.

4. What is a *kittel*?

   (a) Yiddish for "a little cat";   (b) a carrying case for a *dreidel*;   (c) the white robe worn at High Holiday services.

Answers on page 55

5. What is the *Ralbag*?
   (a) a form of transportation used in biblical times;   (b) the name of a rabbi;
   (c) a carrying case for *tefillin*;   (d) the name of a famous Jewish academy of
   learning in Poland.

6. What is "Hagiographa"?
   (a) the name of a Greek emperor who persecuted the Jews;   (b) a geography
   game played in Israel;   (c) the third section of the Hebrew Bible.

7. What is a *shaliach tzibbur* ("messenger of the congregation")?
   (a) a rabbi;   (b) a cantor;   (c) a *shammash*.

8. What is *chanukat ha-bayit*?
   (a) when a Chanukah menorah is lit in a household;   (b) when a builder is finished
   building a new house;   (c) when a mezuzah is put up.

9. What is an *etz chaim* ("tree of life")?
   (a) a Jewish burial society;   (b) the organization that plants trees in Israel;
   (c) each of the wooden rollers to which the Torah scroll is attached;   (d) the
   marriage canopy.

10. What is another word for a *tzedakah* box?
    (a) a *kittel*; (b) a *pushka*; (c) a *pushkin*; (d) a *pisher*.

11. What are *bentschers*?
    (a) kosher butchers; (b) Jewish weightlifters; (c) booklets containing the text of the Grace After Meals; (d) synagogue pews.

12. What is an *aufruf*?
    (a) the calling of a groom-to-be to the Torah on the Shabbat preceding his wedding;
    (b) the noise made by Israeli dogs; (c) Yiddish name for a very religious person;
    (d) the deputy prime minister of Israel.

13. What is a *sheitel*?
    (a) a small ghetto town; (b) a wig worn by Orthodox married women; (c) a velvet-trimmed hat worn by Orthodox men; (d) a fool.

14. What is *karpas*?
    (a) a fish used in making gefilte fish; (b) greens on the seder plate; (c) Hebrew word for *yarmulke*; (d) the cement used in the Temple.

15. What is a *parochet*?
    (a) the bird that Noah sent out to see if the Flood had receded; (b) the partition separating men and women in Orthodox synagogues; (c) an ark curtain; (d) the mixture of apples, nuts, cinnamon, and wine eaten at the Passover seder.

16. What are the *Fier Kashes*?
    (a) the four questions asked at the Passover seder; (b) porridge usually eaten with bowtie-shaped noodles; (c) brand name of one type of Chanukah candle.

17. What is a *wimpel*?
    (a) a kosher fast-food hamburger sold in Israel; (b) a Torah binder; (c) a *cheder* student; (d) a Hasidic melody.

18. What are seraphim and cherubim?
    (a) angels; (b) biblical musical instruments; (c) Jews from Spain and Germany.

19. What is the Decalogue?
    (a) the ten men in a *minyan*; (b) the Ten Commandments; (c) the ten plagues.

20. What are the *kamatz, patach, segol,* and *chirik*?
    (a) Torah ornaments; (b) Hebrew vowels; (c) Passover recipes.

1. Which one of the following is *not* a book of the Bible?
   (**a**) the Book of Esther;   (**b**) the Book of Jonah;   (**c**) the Book of Judith;   (**d**) the Book of Daniel.

2. Which one of the following is *not* the name of a person mentioned in the Bible?
   (**a**) Dodo;   (**b**) Nun;   (**c**) Ham;   (**d**) Bob.

3. What are the only two books of the Bible in which the name of God does not appear?

4. Which did God create first, the sun and moon or the earth and seas?

5. What is the first of the 613 *mitzvot*?

6. Haftarah readings are taken from which part of the Bible?
   (**a**) the Torah;   (**b**) the Prophets;   (**c**) the Writings.

7. Which book of the Bible has only one chapter?

8. Which one of the following is *not* the name of one of the twelve tribes of Israel?
   (**a**) Reuben;   (**b**) Joshua;   (**c**) Gad;   (**d**) Asher.

Answers on page 55

9. In which book of the Bible does Samson appear?
   (a) Judges;   (b) Exodus;   (c) Genesis;   (d) Samuel.

10. How many children did Noah have?

11. How long did the rains of the Great Flood last?

12. The patriarch Abraham came from Ur, which was a city in _____.
    (a) Mesopotamia;   (b) Canaan;   (c) Babylonia;   (d) Egypt.

13. There were three patriarchs (Abraham, Isaac, and Jacob) and four matriarchs (Sarah, Rebecca, Leah, and Rachel). All of these seven ancestors but one are buried in the Cave of Machpelah. Who is not buried there?

14. Who was Rachel and Leah's father?
    (a) Laban;   (b) David;   (c) Terah;   (d) Isaac.

15. What was commanded by God to be made of gopher wood, 300 cubits in length, 50 cubits in breadth, and 30 cubits in height?

16. Who was the eldest, Moses, his brother Aaron, or their sister Miriam?

17. Who buried Moses?

18. According to tradition, one of the following Bible heroes never died but ascended to heaven in a fiery chariot and will return at the end of days. Who is it?
(a) Moses;   (b) Abraham;   (c) Elijah;   (d) David.

19. What procedure did Ruth undergo to convert to Judaism?
(a) She went to a *mikveh*;   (b) She appeared before a *bet din*;   (c) She took lessons to learn about the religion;   (d) She made a statement of allegiance.

20. Parshandatha, Dalphon, Aspatha, Poratha, Adalia, Aridatha, Parmashta, Arisai, Aridai, and Vaizatha were the sons of _____.
(a) Jacob;   (b) Noah;   (c) Haman;   (d) Abraham.

Sukkot Answers

1. Passover and Shavuot. **2.** Yes. **3.** Dark brown. **4.** The roof. **5.** (c) animal skins. **6.** No. (It is not a permanent dwelling place and therefore does not require a *mezuzah*.) **7.** (a) 4′ × 4′. **8.** (c) the Israelites after the Exodus from Egypt. **9.** False. (It can have as little as two and a half walls.) **10.** (a) roof. **11.** True. **12.** David. **13.** The *etrog*. **14.** The *lulav*. **15.** The left. **16.** East. **17.** Heart. **18.** No. **19.** (d) an *etrog* requiring two hands to hold it. **20.** (b) Yom Ha-Zicharon.

"What Is . . . ?" Answers

1. (b) nickname for the area of Jewish resort hotels in the Catskill Mountains. **2.** (c) swaying of the body during prayer. **3.** (c) a picnic held by Moroccan Jews the day after Passover. **4.** (c) the white robe worn at High Holiday services. **5.** (b) the name of a rabbi (Rabbi Levi ben Gershom, also known as Gersonides). **6.** (c) the third section of the Hebrew Bible (also known as the Writings, or Kethuvim). **7.** (b) a cantor. **8.** (c) when a *mezuzah* is put up. **9.** (c) each of the wooden rollers to which the Torah scroll is attached. **10.** (b) a *pushka*. **11.** (c) booklets containing the text of the Grace After Meals. **12.** (a) the calling of a groom-to-be to the Torah on the Shabbat preceding his wedding. **13.** (b) a wig worn by Orthodox married women. **14.** (b) greens on the seder plate. **15.** (c) an ark curtain. **16.** (a) the four questions asked at the Passover seder. **17.** (b) a Torah binder. **18.** (a) angels. **19.** (b) the Ten Commandments. **20.** (b) Hebrew vowels.

All About the Bible Answers

1. (c) the Book of Judith. **2.** (d) Bob. (Dodo was the father of one of David's warriors, Nun was Joshua's father, and Ham was Noah's son.) **3.** Esther and the Song of Songs. **4.** The earth and seas (on the third day; the sun and moon were created on the fourth day). **5.** To have children ("Be fruitful and multiply"). **6.** (b) the Prophets. **7.** Obadiah. **8.** (b) Joshua. **9.** (a) Judges. **10.** Three sons. **11.** Forty days and forty nights. **12.** (a) Mesopotamia. **13.** Rachel. (She is buried on the road to Bethlehem, where she weeps for her children in exile as she lies alone by the roadside.) **14.** (a) Laban. **15.** Noah's ark. **16.** Miriam. **17.** God Himself. **18.** (c) Elijah. **19.** (d) She made a statement of allegiance. ("Your people shall be my people; your God, my God.") **20.** (c) Haman.

1. According to the collection of legends known as the Aggadah, how old were Adam and Eve when they were created?

(a) thirteen years old; (b) twenty years old; (c) thirty-five years old; (d) forty years old.

2. How old is a boy when he is first counted as part of a *minyan*?

3. How old was Abraham when he was circumcised?

(a) eight days; (b) thirteen years; (c) forty-five years; (d) ninety-nine years.

4. How old was Anne Frank when she began her diary?

(a) eleven; (b) twelve; (c) thirteen; (d) fourteen.

5. Moses died at the age of 120. How old was Aaron when he died?

(a) 82; (b) 95; (c) 123; (d) 207.

6. According to custom, how old is a male when he first puts on the ritual under-garment (*tzitzit*)?

(a) thirteen; (b) twenty; (c) the age at which he gets married; (d) the age at which he begins to talk.

Answers on page 69

7. How old are the young men and women who are confirmed in Reform and some Conservative congregations?

8. How old was Rabbi Akiva when he started school?
   (a) three;   (b) seven;   (c) thirteen;   (d) forty.

9. How old do you have to be to vote in Israel?

10. According to the treatise Megillah, how old was Esther when she won the beauty contest and the queenship?
    (a) thirteen;   (b) seventeen;   (c) twenty-five;   (d) forty.

11. How old was Mordecai Anilewicz when he died fighting the Nazis in the Warsaw Ghetto Uprising?
    (a) twenty-four;   (b) thirty;   (c) thirty-six;   (d) forty-two.

12. According to the rabbis, how old is a child when he or she is ready for school?

13. How old was Sarah when she gave birth to Isaac?

14. According to ancient Jewish law, how old is a young man when he is first expected to pay taxes and fight in a war?
    (a) thirteen;   (b) fifteen;   (c) twenty;   (d) twenty-one.

15. How old was Ishmael when he was circumcised?
    (a) eight days;   (b) thirteen years;   (c) sixteen years;   (d) Ishmael wasn't circumcised.

16. How old was Albert Einstein when he published his initial Theory of Relativity?
    (a) forty-five;   (b) thirty-two;   (c) twenty-six;   (d) nineteen.

17. How old was Chaim Weizmann when he became the president of Israel?

18. How old was Yonatan Netanyahu when he died rescuing the Jewish hostages in the Entebbe raid?
    (a) twenty-seven;   (b) thirty;   (c) thirty-two;   (d) thirty-five.

19. How old was Theodor Herzl when he died?
    (a) eighty-one;   (b) sixty-two;   (c) fifty-nine;   (d) forty-four.

20. How old must you be before your testimony is acceptable in a Jewish court of law?

1. Aron Isak was the first Jew to settle in Sweden. King Gustav III told him that he was free to worship any way he chose. To this, Isak replied:

    (**a**) "*Shema Yisrael*";   (**b**) "Thank you, Your Majesty";   (**c**) "In that case, I need nine more Jews."

2. Which Jewish comedian said, "I don't care to belong to any social organization that will accept me as a member"?

3. What other Myerson said to Bess, "So you're the famous Myerson girl"?

4. Which Nobel Prize winner, when told that his award would be presented by the king of Sweden, said, "Good. I have never had the opportunity to say the blessing one makes upon seeing a king"?

    (**a**) Albert Einstein;   (**b**) S. Y. Agnon;   (**c**) I. L. Peretz;   (**d**) David Ben-Gurion.

5. The saying "From Moses to Moses there was none like Moses" is a tribute to which Moses?

    (**a**) Moses of the Bible;   (**b**) Moses Maimonides;   (**c**) Moses Montefiore;   (**d**) Moses Malone.

6. Who told Moe Berg, major-league catcher for several teams in the 1930s, "You teach me to catch, and I'll teach you mathematics"?

7. Who said, "Unless you can play baseball, you'll never get to be a rabbi in America"?
   (a) Sandy Koufax;   (b) Groucho Marx;   (c) Solomon Schechter;   (d) Howard Cosell.

8. "God bless America, / land that I love, / Stand beside her, and guide her, / Through the night with a light from above" is a quote from a song by
   (a) Irving Berlin;   (b) Oscar Hammerstein II;   (c) George Gershwin;   (d) Emma Lazarus.

9. Who first called the Jews the "people of the book"?
   (a) Mohammed;   (b) Maimonides;   (c) Rashi;   (d) Chaim Weizmann.

10. The words "Proclaim liberty throughout the land unto all the inhabitants thereof," inscribed on the Liberty Bell, are taken from
    (a) the Bible;   (b) a poem by Emma Lazarus;   (c) the Talmud;   (d) a letter written by Haym Salomon to George Washington.

11. "Whoever is for the Lord, follow me!" was the battle cry of the
    (a) Maccabees;   (b) Warsaw Ghetto fighters;   (c) Haganah.

12. Who said, "I am the American Sholem Aleichem"?
    (a) Mark Twain;   (b) Chaim Potok;   (c) Groucho Marx;   (d) O. Henry.

13. Which famous Jewish scientist said, "I shall never believe that God plays dice with the world"?
    (a) Sigmund Freud;   (b) Albert Einstein;   (c) Jonas Salk;   (d) Franz Boas.

14. The sayings "Silence is golden" and "Don't count your chickens before they hatch" come from which book of the Bible?
    (a) Genesis;   (b) Judges;   (c) Psalms;   (d) Proverbs.

15. Who wrote, "The quality of urban air compared to desert or forest air is like polluted water compared to pure, filtered water"?
    (a) Albert Einstein;   (b) Samuel Gompers;   (c) Maimonides.

16. Who wrote the following entry in his diary: "In the same month in which Their Majesties issued the edict that all Jews should be driven out of the kingdom and its territories . . . they gave me the order to undertake with sufficient men my expedition to the Indies"?

17. Where were the Jews first described as a "stiff-necked people"?
    (a) in the Bible;   (b) in Franz Boas's study of the physical similarities of the different races;   (c) in Adolf Hitler's *Mein Kampf*;   (d) in Chaim Nachman Bialik's poetry.

18. Hanging in the Touro Synagogue in Newport, Rhode Island, is a letter from a U.S. president. The letter says, "Happily the Government of the United States . . . gives to bigotry no sanction, to persecution no assistance." Which president wrote this letter?
(**a**) George Washington; (**b**) Abraham Lincoln; (**c**) Franklin D. Roosevelt; (**d**) Ronald Reagan.

19. Who wrote in his diary in 1897, "In Basle I created the Jewish state. Were I to say this aloud, I would be greeted with universal laughter. But perhaps . . . fifty years hence, everybody will perceive it"?

20. Hearst newspaper editor Arthur Brisbane said, "He has done more to conquer anti-Semitism than a thousand textbooks." To whom was Brisbane referring?
(**a**) physicist Albert Einstein; (**b**) comedian Groucho Marx; (**c**) boxer Benny Leonard; (**d**) composer Leonard Bernstein.

1. How many Chanukah candles come in a box?

2. In the song "I Have a Little *Dreidel*," what is the *dreidel* made out of?

3. True or false: The Chanukah story is found in the Bible.

4. What's a *sevivon*?

5. *Chanukah* means
   (a) "lights";   (b)"oil";   (c) "dedication";   (d) "eight."

6. On a Friday night during Chanukah you
   (a) light the Shabbat candles first, then the Chanukah candles;   (b) light the Chanukah candles first, then the Shabbat candles;   (c) light the Shabbat candles, but do not light the Chanukah candles.

7. Which holiday is older, Chanukah or Christmas?

8. How many brothers did Judah Maccabee have?

9. Why would someone give an $18 check for Chanukah rather than a $15 check or a $20 check?

Answers on page 69

Candles, Dreidels— Chanukah!

64

10. True or false: The letters נגהש appear on all *dreidels* throughout the world.

11. When is the *Shehecheyanu* prayer said at Chanukah?

12. What's a *chanukkiah*?

13. Which of the following statements is true?
(a) Chanukah candles are put into the menorah from right to left and lit from left to right;   (b) Chanukah candles are put into the menorah from left to right and lit from right to left;   (c) Chanukah candles are put into the menorah from right to left and lit from right to left;   (d) Chanukah candles are put into the menorah from left to right and lit from left to right.

14. The name *Yehudah Ha-Maccabee* means
(a) "Judah the Hammer";   (b) "Judah the Athlete";   (c) "God will save us";
(d) "Judah will save us."

15. True or false: Shammai argued that one should light eight lights on the first night of Chanukah and steadily diminish the number until there is only one light on the last day.

16. Is the story of Chanukah mentioned in the Mishnah?

17. What is the name of the special prayer added to the *Amidah* and *Birkat Ha-Mazon* on Chanukah?

    (a) *Al Ha-Nissim*;   (b) *Al Chet*;   (c) *Avinu Malkenu*.

18. What Chanukah food is called *levivot* by Israelis?

19. Which person in the Chanukah story was known as Epiphanes?

20. What is a synonym for the terms *fasputshes* and *pontshkes*, which are used by some Ashkenazim?

1. Approximately how many Jewish physicians are there in the United States?
   (a) 100,000;   (b) 65,000;   (c) 30,000;   (d) 15,000.

2. How many volumes does the *Encyclopedia Judaica* have?

3. How many people signed Israel's Declaration of Independence?
   (a) 120;   (b) 50;   (c) 38;   (d) 27.

4. What percentage of its wine does Manischewitz sell to Jews?
   (a) 50 per cent;   (b) 75 per cent;   (c) 10 per cent;   (d) 90 per cent.

5. How many blessings make up the Eighteen Benedictions?

6. How long were the Jews in Egypt?
   (a) 40 years;   (b) 70 years;   (c) 210 years;   (d) 500 years.

7. How many Jews were there in Israel in 1948?
   (a) 1 million;   (b) 650,000;   (c) 250,000;   (d) 50,000.

8. How many years did King David rule?
   (a) ten;   (b) forty;   (c) fifty;   (d) seventy.

9. What was the average amount of money brought to America by Russian-Jewish immigrants in the 1890s?
   (a) $100.00;   (b) $52.75;   (c) $27.08;   (d) $15.50.

10. How many is "quadruple *chai*"?

11. How many books of the Mishnah are there?

12. How many people must witness the signing of a *ketubah*?

13. How old was Adam when he died?
   (a) 147;   (b) 930;   (c) 110;   (d) 950.

14. How many angels are mentioned by name in the Bible?

15. Of the 613 commandments, how many deal with medical topics (washing, care of the skin, dietetic and sanitary regulations, isolation and quarantine, etc.)?

16. How many tribes of Israel were there?

17. What was the Jewish population of Canada in the year 1846?
   (a) 50,000;   (b) 10,000;   (c) 5,000;   (d) 200.

18. How many career strikeouts did Sandy Koufax have?
    (a) 5,348;   (b) 4,213;   (c) 2,396;   (d) 1,250.

19. What is the total number of verses in the Torah?
    (a) 8,064;   (b) 6,530;   (c) 5,845;   (d) 1,299.

20. How many times did Albert Einstein win the Nobel Prize?

**Numbers,
Numbers,
Numbers**

68

"How Old . . . ?" Answers

1. (b) twenty years old. **2.** Thirteen. **3. (d)** ninety-nine years. **4. (c)** thirteen. (She got it as a gift for her thirteenth birthday.) **5. (c)** 123. **6. (d)** the age at which he begins to talk. **7.** Sixteen. **8. (d)** forty. **9.** Eighteen. **10. (d)** forty. **11. (a)** twenty-four. **12.** Five. **13.** Ninety. **14. (c)** twenty. **15. (b)** thirteen years. **16. (c)** twenty-six. **17.** Seventy-four. **18. (b)** thirty. **19. (d)** forty-four. **20.** Thirteen.

You Can Say That Again Answers

1. (c) "In that case, I need nine more Jews." (That's how the first *minyan* was assembled in Sweden.) **2.** Groucho Marx. **3.** Golda Meir (formerly Goldie Mabovitz Myerson). **4. (b)** S. Y. Agnon. **5. (b)** Moses Maimonides. **6.** Albert Einstein. **7. (c)** Solomon Schechter (who was then president of the Jewish Theological Seminary of America). **8. (a)** Irving Berlin. **9. (a)** Mohammed. **10. (a)** the Bible. **11. (a)** Maccabees. **12. (a)** Mark Twain. **13. (b)** Albert Einstein. **14. (d)** Proverbs. **15. (c)** Maimonides. **16.** Christopher Columbus. **17. (a)** in the Bible. **18. (a)** George Washington. **19.** Theodor Herzl. **20. (c)** boxer Benny Leonard.

Candles, Dreidels—Chanukah! Answers

1. Forty-four. **2.** Clay. **3.** False. **4.** It's the Hebrew word for *dreidel*. **5. (c)** "dedication." **6. (b)** light the Chanukah candles first, then the Shabbat candles. **7.** Chanukah. **8.** Four. **9.** Because 18 is the numerical value of the two letters that make up the Hebrew word חי (*chai*), meaning "life." **10.** False. (נגהש stand for "*Nes gadol hayah sham*," "A great miracle happened there." Israeli *dreidels* have a פ, not a ש, for "*Nes gadol hayah po*," "A great miracle happened *here*.") **11.** On the first night. **12.** A Chanukah menorah. **13. (a)** Chanukah candles are put into the menorah from right to left and lit from left to right. **14. (a)** "Judah the Hammer." **15.** True. **16.** No. **17. (a)** *Al Ha-Nissim*. **18.** Latkes, or potato pancakes. **19.** Antiochus. **20.** Latkes, or potato pancakes.

Numbers, Numbers, Numbers Answers

1. (c) 30,000. **2.** Sixteen. **3. (c)** 38. **4. (c)** 10 per cent. **5.** Nineteen. (One was added later.) **6. (c)** 210 years. **7. (b)** 650,000. **8. (b)** forty. **9. (d)** $15.50. **10.** Seventy-two ("*chai*" = 18). **11.** Six. **12.** Two. **13. (b)** 930. **14.** Two (Gabriel and Michael). **15.** 213. **16.** Twelve. **17. (d)** 200. **18. (c)** 2,396. **19. (c)** 5,845. **20.** Once.

1. True or false: Mormons call any non-Mormon a gentile; therefore, to a Mormon a Jew is a gentile.

2. *Ieu, Ieuu, Iwe, Iow, Iue, Ive,* and *Iewe* were Old English spellings of which word?

3. Which term was coined by Nathan Birnbaum in 1893?
   (a) Lower East Side;   (b) Zionism;   (c) Industrial Revolution.

4. The expression "the *goldene medina*" was used to refer to _____ .

5. The *kinnor,* the *nebel,* the *chalil,* and the *chatzotzerah* were _____ .
   (a) four biblical musical instruments;   (b) four types of kosher animals mentioned in the Bible;   (c) the titles of four officials of the Jewish community during the Golden Age in Spain.

6. In the expression "Hip! Hip! Hooray!" the word "Hip" is based on three initials that stand for _____ .
   (a) a phrase from the Bible;   (b) an anti-Semitic slogan;   (c) the name of a famous rabbi.

7. When is *"Shavuah tov"* said?

Answers on page 79

8. What do *ben*, *bar*, and *ibn* mean?

9. What four-sided spinning top is called a *trendel* by Jews of Germany, Bohemia, and Hungary, and a *werfel* by other European Jews?

10. *Chavurah*, *gdud*, *plugah*, and *kvutzah* were all early names for the _____.
   (a) *minyan*;   **(b)** Knesset;   **(c)** *kibbutz*;   **(d)** Lubavitcher Hasidim.

11. *Judiaria* in Portugal, *Juiverie* in northern France, and *Judenviertel* and *Judengasse* in Germany were names of _____.
   (a) synagogues;   **(b)** *yeshivot*;   **(c)** Jewish ghettos.

12. *Aelia Capitolina* was the Roman name for _____.

13. The Yiddish word *benshn*, meaning the "Grace After Meals," comes from what language?

14. When your grandmother says *"Ess, ess, mein kindt,"* what does she want you to do?

15. True or false: A gentile who immigrates to Israel, like a Jewish immigrant, is called an *oleh*.

16. The Yiddish term *shul* is derived from the German *Schule*, which means _____.
    (a) school;   (b) prayer;   (c) sanctuary;   (d) sermon.

17. What's the difference between a bagel and a bialy?

18. Which term of endearment is a diminutive of *bubbe*, the Yiddish word for grandmother?

19. What is the phrase used by Jews attempting to ward off the evil eye?

20. Which of the following is the term for an Israeli old-age home?
    (a) *bet sefer*;   (b) *bet knesset*;   (c) *bet shimush*;   (d) *bet horim*.

How many of the following Jewish objects can you identify?

1.

2.

3.

4.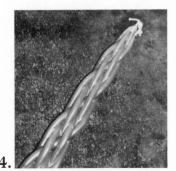

5.

6.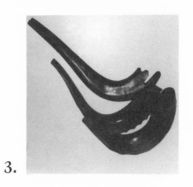

Answers on page 79

7.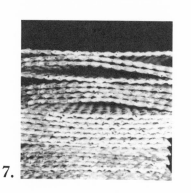

8.

9.

10.

11.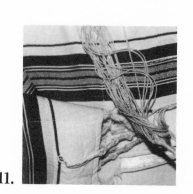

12.

13. Give the Yiddish, Hebrew, and English names of this one.

Give the English and Hebrew names of these.

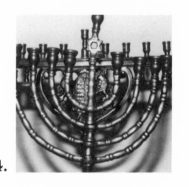

14.

15.

16.
Give the Yiddish name for the round objects floating in the soup.

1. Which Jewish symbol is on the official seal of Israel?

2. Which Jewish symbol can be described as "a hexagram formed by two equilateral triangles"?

3. The two blue stripes on the Israeli flag were modeled after the stripes on _____ .

   (a) the American flag;   (b) a *tallit*;   (c) a zebra.

4. Which is older, the nine-branched menorah or the seven-branched menorah?

5. What are phylacteries?

6. True or false: To wear a *mezuzah* on a chain around your neck is a Torah commandment.

7. Which one of the following rooms requires a *mezuzah*?
   (a) bathroom;   (b) closet;   (c) laundry room;   (d) kitchen.

8. If your *mezuzah* falls off its doorpost, do you say the blessing over the *mezuzah* when you rehang it?

Answers on page 79

9. Which one does not belong?
   (**a**) *tzitzit*;   (**b**) *shatnez*;   (**c**) *tallit katan*;   (**d**) *arbah kanfot*.

10. What is the plural of *tzitzit*?

11. Which is put on first, the *tallit* or the *tefillin*?

12. How should the parchment scroll inside a *mezuzah* be rolled?
   (**a**) left to right;   (**b**) right to left;   (**c**) top to bottom;   (**d**) bottom to top.

13. Is a *kippah* worn on the head, the arm, or the shoulders?

14. Which Jewish symbol is older, the menorah or the *Magen David*?

15. Which one of the following documents does not have to be written by a scribe?
   (**a**) a *mezuzah*;   (**b**) a *ketubah*;   (**c**) the inside of *tefillin*;   (**d**) a Torah scroll.

16. On which arm does a right-handed man wear *tefillin*?

17. How often do you have to inspect your *mezuzah* to make sure that the writing on the parchment scroll hasn't worn off?
   (**a**) once every year;   (**b**) once every two years;   (**c**) once every seven years;
   (**d**) twice every seven years.

18. What is the symbol for the Israeli Red Cross?

19. Which ceremonial object is not kissed?
    (a) *tallit*;   (b) *mezuzah*;   (c) Torah;   (d) *kiddush* cup.

20. A pious Jewish man is buried with his _____.
    (a) *tallit*;   (b) *mezuzah*;   (c) *ketubah*;   (d) *siddur*.

This and That

78

Words, Words, Words Answers

1. True. **2.** Jew. **3.** (**b**) Zionism. **4.** The United States. (It means "the golden country.") **5.** (**a**) four biblical musical instruments. **6.** (**b**) an anti-Semitic slogan (the Latin expression *Hierosolyma Est Perdita*, "Jerusalem is destroyed"). **7.** After Shabbat. It means "Have a good week." **8.** They all mean "son of." **9.** The *dreidel*. **10.** (**c**) *kibbutz*. **11.** (**c**) Jewish ghettos. **12.** Jerusalem. **13.** Latin (from the word for "benediction"). **14.** Eat. ("Eat, eat, my child.") **15.** False. The word for a gentile immigrant is *hagirah*. **16.** (**a**) school. **17.** A bagel is a hard roll with a hole in the middle; a bialy is made of softer dough, contains onions, and has an indentation in its center instead of a hole. **18.** *Bubeleh.* **19.** *Kayn aynhoreh.* **20.** (**d**) *bet horim.*

What Is It? Answers

1. Shabbat candles. **2.** Groggers (Purim noisemakers). **3.** *Shofars.* **4.** Havdalah candle. **5.** Challot. **6.** *Megillat Esther* (the Purim Megillah). **7.** Matzot. **8.** Bagel. **9.** *Kiddush* cups. **10.** Chanukah candles. **11.** *Tallit.* **12.** *Tefillin* bags. **13.** *Yarmulke* (Yiddish), *kippah* (Hebrew), skullcap (English). **14.** Chanukah menorahs (English), *chanukkiot* (Hebrew). **15.** Phylacteries (English), *tefillin* (Hebrew). **16.** *Knaidlach* (matzah balls).

This and That Answers

1. The menorah. **2.** The *Magen David* (Star of David) or "Jewish star." **3.** (**b**) a *tallit.* **4.** The seven-branched menorah is older. **5.** *Tefillin.* **6.** False. (In fact, some rabbis object to it.) **7.** (**d**) kitchen. **8.** Yes. **9.** (**b**) *shatnez.* (The others are synonyms for the fringed ritual undergarment worn by men; *shatnez* is the biblical injunction against wearing a garment made of a mixture of wool and linen.) **10.** *Tzitziot.* **11.** The *tallit.* **12.** (**a**) left to right (so that when it is unrolled, the first words appear first). **13.** The head. (*Kippah* is the Hebrew word for *yarmulke*.) **14.** The menorah. **15.** (**b**) a *ketubah.* **16.** The left arm. **17.** (**d**) twice every seven years. **18.** The *Magen David.* **19.** (**d**) *kiddush* cup. **20.** (**a**) *tallit.*

1.Who were the only two American presidents able to read Hebrew?
(a) Abraham Lincoln; (b) James Madison; (c) Franklin D. Roosevelt;
(d) James Garfield.

2.What Hebrew letter begins the Ten Commandments?

3.What is the traditional response to the greeting "*Shalom aleichem*"?

4. In Hebrew, *me* is "who," *who* is "he," and *he* is "she." What is "what"?

5. All but one of the following English words are derived from Hebrew. Which one is the exception?
(a) jubilee; (b) amen; (c) synagogue; (d) sabbath.

6.True or false: Some Christian churches in Israel conduct services in Hebrew.

7.The town of Salem, Massachusetts, was named for a Hebrew word. Which word?

8.Two letters in the *Shema* prayer are written larger than the others. Which two letters?
(a) *aleph* and *dalet*; (b) *ayin* and *dalet*; (c) *shin* and *dalet*; (d) *yud* and *shin*.

Answers on page 88

9. Which word, said at the climax of a popular board game, is a combination of the Hebrew words *shach* ("sheik") and *met* ("dead")?

10. *B'teavon* is the Hebrew equivalent of which French expression?
    (**a**) "Au revoir"; (**b**) "Bonjour"; (**c**) "Bon appétit"; (**d**) "Vive la France."

11. Who of the following would be considered a *jinjy* (ג'ינג'י) or *jinjit* (ג'ינג'ית)
in Israel?
    (**a**) Golda Meir; (**b**) Little Orphan Annie; (**c**) Buddy Hackett; (**d**) Bozo the Clown; (**e**) Julius Erving; (**f**) Lucille Ball.

12. All but one of the following words commonly used in everyday English are actually Yiddish words. Which one is the exception?
    (**a**) conniption; (**b**) bubkes; (**c**) goniff; (**d**) kishke.

13. What is the most frequently used letter in the Five Books of Moses?

14. If you wrote down the first, middle, and last letters of the Hebrew alphabet, in that order, the word that you would make would mean _____.
    (**a**) truth; (**b**) mother; (**c**) amen; (**d**) I.

15. Which one of the following universities does *not* have Hebrew letters on its coat of arms?

(a) Yeshiva University;   (b) Brandeis University;   (c) Yale University;   (d) University of Pennsylvania.

16. The term *sabra* is used to mean a native-born Israeli, but it also has anóther meaning. What is it?

17. Which letter is at the exact middle of the Torah?

18. At various times Ladino has been spoken in all but one of these countries. Which one is the exception?

(a) France;   (b) Australia;   (c) Yugoslavia;   (d) Romania.

19. The first Yiddish newspaper in the world was published in 1686–1687. Where was it published?

(a) Germany;   (b) Poland;   (c) Amsterdam;   (d) New Amsterdam.

20. True or false: When the Soviet Union was first founded, Yiddish was made one of the sixty-odd official languages of the country.

1. Which of the following countries has never had a Jewish head of government?
   (a) India;   (b) China;   (c) Hungary;   (d) Austria.

2. Who was the first Jewish U.S. secretary of state?

3. Whom did David Ben-Gurion call "the only real man in my cabinet"?

4. Who was the first Jew to be elected mayor of New York City?

5. Which one of the following people did *not* sign Israel's Declaration of Independence?
   (a) Abba Eban;   (b) Rachel Cohen;   (c) Fritz Bernstein;   (d) Rabbi Wolf Gold.

6. Who is more powerful, the Israeli president or the Israeli prime minister?

7. The first Jewish member of the New York Bar and one of the founders (and vice president) of the Jeffersonian Democratic party in 1795 was _____.
   (a) Adam Adom;   (b) Moses Meeses;   (c) Samson Simson;   (d) Isaac Isaacman.

8. Who was the first Israeli ambassador to Russia?

9. True or false: Every Israeli prime minister has been born in Israel.

Answers on page 88

10. Which one of the following U.S. presidents did not have any Jewish cabinet members?

   (**a**) Theodore Roosevelt; (**b**) Herbert Hoover; (**c**) John F. Kennedy; (**d**) Jimmy Carter.

11. Which one of the following Jews was not a member of the U.S. Congress?
   (**a**) Bella Abzug; (**b**) Jacob Javits; (**c**) Arlen Specter; (**d**) Cyrus Adler.

12. René Joel Simon Mayer, premier of France in 1953, was one of the founders of which French institution?

   (**a**) the Louvre; (**b**) Air France; (**c**) the Cordon Bleu school of cooking; (**d**) the Bastille.

13. Who was Israel's first president?

14. How many Knesset members are there?

15. When a journalist asked Golda Meir what it felt like to be a woman foreign minister, Meir replied _____.

   (**a**) "It is a great honor"; (**b**) "It's no big deal"; (**c**) "How should I know? I have never been a male foreign minister."

16. Every year statesman Oscar Straus would send a special gift to President Grover Cleveland. What was the gift?

(a) a case of matzot;   (b) a quart of chicken soup;   (c) a bottle of Carmel wine; (d) a Jewish calendar.

17. True or false: No Israeli political party has ever won an absolute majority of the seats in the Knesset.

18. Moses Alexander was the first Jew to be elected governor of a state. Which state did he govern?

(a) New York;   (b) Florida;   (c) Idaho;   (d) Rhode Island.

19. Sir Joshua Abraham Hassan was the chief minister of which country?

(a) England;   (b) New Zealand;   (c) Gibraltar;   (d) Wales.

20. How many candidates were there in the first election to the Knesset in January 1949?

(a) 57;   (b) 120;   (c) 753;   (d) 1,288.

1. Name the Five Books of Moses.

2. The Hebrew word for the ornaments used to crown the Torah, *rimmonim*, is also the word for which fruit?

3. True or false: The Torah scroll contains no punctuation or vowels.

4. Can a scribe write a Torah in gold ink?

5. A Torah pointer is usually shaped like which part of the body?

6. The Torah ends with the story of the death of _____.

7. True or false: Sephardic Jews read from their Torah scroll without removing it from its case.

8. How many columns are there in a Torah scroll?
   (a) 613;   (b) 572;   (c) 248;   (d) 127.

9. Do you have to stand when a Torah is being removed from the ark even if you can't see the Torah?

10. Should one violate the Sabbath to prevent a Torah scroll from being destroyed?

Answers on page 88

11. Who receives the first *aliyah* when the Torah is read in synagogue?

12. True or false: The Torah is put back into the ark before the Haftarah is read.

13. How many Torah portions are there?

14. Why don't we make Torah ornaments out of gold?

15. In which of the Five Books of Moses does Moses not appear?

16. Before writing each word of the Torah on the parchment, the scribe must _____.

    (a) pronounce it;   (b) say a prayer;   (c) bend his knees;   (d) wash his hands.

17. Can the Torah be read if less than a *minyan* is present?

18. Which book of the Torah gets its English name from the census of the people in Chapters 1, 3, 4, and 26?

19. According to Jewish law, if you see a Torah drop, what should you do for forty days?

20. What should a Torah reader do if he reads a word incorrectly?

Hebrew, Yiddish, and Ladino Answers

1. (b) James Madison and **(d)** James Garfield. **2.** *Aleph.* **3.** *"Aleichem shalom."* **4.** *Mah.* **5. (c)** synagogue. (It is from Greek.) **6.** True. (Hebrew is an official language.) **7.** *Shalom.* **8. (b)** *ayin* and *dalet.* **9.** Checkmate. **10. (c)** *"Bon appétit."* **11. (b)** Little Orphan Annie, **(d)** Bozo the Clown, and **(f)** Lucille Ball. (*Jinjy* means "redhead.") **12. (a)** conniption. **13.** *Vav.* (It occurs 76,922 times out of the 815,280 letters in the Torah.) **14. (a)** truth (**אמת**). **15. (d)** University of Pennsylvania. **16.** Cactus plant. **17.** A *vav* (in the word *gahon* ["belly"] in Lev. 11:42). **18. (b)** Australia. **19. (c)** Amsterdam. **20.** True.

Jews in Politics Answers

1. (b) China. **2.** Judah P. Benjamin (1811–1884) was appointed secretary of state by Confederate president Jefferson Davis. **3.** Golda Meir. **4.** Abraham Beame. **5. (a)** Abba Eban. **6.** The Israeli prime minister. **7. (c)** Samson Simson. **8.** Golda Meir. **9.** False. **10. (b)** Herbert Hoover. **11. (d)** Cyrus Adler. **12. (b)** Air France. **13.** Chaim Weizmann. **14.** 120. **15. (c)** "How should I know? I have never been a male foreign minister." **16. (a)** a case of matzot. **17.** True. **18. (c)** Idaho. **19. (c)** Gibraltar. **20. (d)** 1,288.

The Great Torah Quiz Answers

1. Genesis, Exodus, Leviticus, Numbers, Deuteronomy (or *Bereshit, Shemot, Vayikra, Bamidbar, Dvarim*). **2.** Pomegranates. **3.** True. **4.** No. **5.** The hand. **6.** Moses. **7.** True. **8. (c)** 248. **9.** Yes (Torah ornaments have bells so you can *hear* the Torah being taken from the ark and know when it's time to stand.) **10.** Yes. **11.** A *kohen.* **12.** False. **13.** Fifty-four. **14.** Because gold was the material used in the building of the Golden Calf. **15.** Genesis. **16. (a)** pronounce it. **17.** No. **18.** Numbers. **19.** Fast. **20.** Repeat the word correctly, then continue.

1. Which French automobile is named after a Jew?

2. Which one of the following companies was *not* founded by a Jew?
   (a) Frito-Lay;   (b) Ex-Lax Co.;   (c) Jordache jeans;   (d) Book-of-the-Month Club.

3. Which one of the following was *not* invented by a Jew?
   (a) the microphone;   (b) the bifocal lens;   (c) the Polaroid camera.

4. Which Nobel Prize–winning author added a middle name derived from his mother's first name to avoid confusion with his brother, also an author, who had the same first initial?
   (a) I. B. Singer;   (b) I. L. Peretz;   (c) S. Y. Agnon;   (d) A. B. Yehoshua.

5. What was the Soncino family famous for?

6. When the Temple stood in Jerusalem, which direction did it face?

7. If somebody tells you to go to Azazel, he is _____.
   (a) suggesting a place to visit on your trip to Israel;   (b) wishing you good luck;
   (c) probably mad at you.

8. Where was B'nai B'rith founded?
   (a) Baltimore;   (b) Germany;   (c) New York's Lower East Side;   (d) Cincinnati.

9. Where do Litvaks come from?

10. What's another name for the Festival of Booths?

11. True or false: The Oral Law has never been written down.

12. During Temple times, what was the only day of the year on which the High Priest entered the Holy of Holies?

13. Nelly Sachs, a German-born poet, received the Nobel Prize for literature in 1966. Her best-known writings were on which subject?
  (**a**) Israel;   (**b**) the Holocaust;   (**c**) the Jewish holidays; (**d**) love and romance.

14. Which one of the Ten Plagues comes next?
  blood, frogs, gnats, —————.

15. Which 3 of the 613 commandments *cannot* be broken, even to save a life?

16. What was brought to the Temple on each of the Omer days between Pesach and Shavuot?
  (**a**) a *shofar*;   (**b**) barley;   (**c**) wine.

17. The abbreviation *Besht* stands for _____.
    (a) the three sections of the Bible; (b) an Israeli political party; (c) one way to conjugate Hebrew verbs; (d) the name of the founder of Hasidism.

18. Which Jewish scientist discovered vitamins?
    (a) Albert Einstein; (b) Casimir Funk; (c) Jonas Salk; (d) Moses Maimonides.

19. According to Maimonides, which type of charity is better, taking a poor person on as a business partner or giving him money even before he asks for it?

20. The abbreviation ORT stands for _____.
    (a) Organization of Religious Teachers; (b) three Russian words meaning "Organization for Rehabilitation and Training"; (c) three Hebrew words meaning "Help Through Work"; (d) Organization of Reform Temples.

1. What was Esther's Hebrew name?

2. Who was queen before Esther?

3. In which city was King Ahasuerus's palace?

4. How did Haman determine the day the Jews were to be abolished?
   (**a**) He read the stars;   (**b**) He had a dream;   (**c**) He drew lots.

5. The Fast of Esther is observed for one day, the day before Purim. How many days did Esther actually fast?

6. Does the Fast of Esther begin at sunrise or sunset?

7. On Purim it is customary to get so silly that you can't tell the difference between which two people in the Purim story?

8. Is it permissible to decorate the Megillah with pictures?

9. When the Megillah is read on Purim, the verses listing the ten sons of Haman are read _____.
   (**a**) very slowly;   (**b**) in one breath;   (**c**) under one's breath.

Answers on page 98

10. What does the word *Purim* mean?

11. From which language does the name *Mordecai* come?
    (a) Hebrew;   (b) Babylonian;   (c) Greek;   (d) Yiddish.

12. What is a Purim *seudah*?

13. What is a *Purim shpiel*?
    (a) the reading of the Megillah;   (b) another name for hamantaschen;   (c) a Purim
    play;   (d) Yiddish term for the custom of giving *shalach manot*.

14. *Ozen Haman* is the Hebrew term for _____.

15. Besides hamantaschen, what other food is traditionally eaten at Purim?
    (a) *kreplach*;   (b) knishes;   (c) *knaidlach*;   (d) kasha.

16. What is the minimum number of food items you must give on Purim in order to
    fulfill the *mitzvah* of *mishloach manot*?

17. True or false: The Scroll of Esther is not the only megillah.

18. Which country has a tomb where, according to tradition, Mordecai and Esther are buried?

19. Who was Zeresh?

20. What is known as *orrechi d'Aman* in Italy?

1. Which one of the following people was never arrested?
   (a) Menachem Begin;   (b) Haym Salomon;   (c) Rabbi Akiva;   (d) Theodor Herzl.

2. Which of the following groups has never ruled the city of Jerusalem?
   (a) the Greeks;   (b) the Persians;   (c) the Romans;   (d) the Argentinians.

3. Which king was also known as Xerxes?
   (a) Antiochus;   (b) Ahasuerus;   (c) Ramses II;   (d) Herod.

4. The first Jewish book to be printed on a printing press (Italy, 1475) was
_____.
   (a) the Bible;   (b) the prayer book;   (c) Rashi's commentary on the Bible;
   (d) the Talmud.

5. Were the inhabitants of the *shtetls* Ashkenazim or Sephardim?

6. In what country did the Golden Age of the Jews flourish in medieval times?

7. When was the term *anti-Semitism* first used?
   (a) 70 C.E.;   (b) 1495;   (c) 1879;   (d) 1915.

8. Who was Philo?

Answers on page 98

9. Who ruled Palestine during the Hellenistic period?
   (a) the Greeks; (b) the Persians; (c) the Babylonians; (d) the Assyrians.

10. Which world-famous Jew was asked, but declined, to run for president of Israel in 1952, after the death of Chaim Weizmann?
    (a) Jacob Javits; (b) Albert Einstein; (c) Abba Eban; (d) Henry Kissinger.

11. Who were the enemies of the Bar Kochba revolt?
    (a) the Greeks; (b) the Romans; (c) the Babylonians; (d) the Assyrians.

12. Shabbetai Zevi claimed to be _____.

13. What European city was known as the "New Jerusalem" in the seventeenth and eighteenth centuries?

14. How many years did Jewish "recruits" have to serve in Czar Nicholas I's Russian army?

15. The Dreyfus Affair started when the French-Jewish officer Alfred Dreyfus was accused of being a _____.

16. Which Nazi leader had at one time a Jewish landlady, a Jewish cook, and a Jewish family physician?

17. Which one of these leaders tried to get rid of the Jews in the territory that he ruled?

   (**a**) Alexander the Great;   (**b**) Charlemagne;   (**c**) Peter Stuyvesant.

18. The words to the Yiddish-socialist theme song "All Men Are Brothers" were written by _____.

   (**a**) Julius and Ethel Rosenberg;   (**b**) Karl Marx;   (**c**) I. L. Peretz;   (**d**) Samuel Gompers.

19. When Moses Montefiore was knighted by Queen Victoria, what word was engraved on the coat of arms that she gave him?

   (**a**) "Torah";   (**b**) "*Tzedakah*";   (**c**) "Jerusalem";   (**d**) "*Chai*."

20. On July 4, 1976, the Israeli army rescued 105 hostages who were being held in an airport in Uganda. The event became known as the Entebbe raid. *Entebbe* was the name of _____.

Mishmash II Answers

1. The Citroën (after André-Gustave Citroën, the "Henry Ford of France"). **2.** (a) Frito-Lay. **3.** (b) the bifocal lens (invented by Benjamin Franklin). The microphone was invented by Emile Berliner, and the Polaroid camera was invented by Edward Land. **4.** (a) I. B. Singer. **5.** Publishing a prayer book. **6.** West. **7.** (c) probably mad at you. (Azazel is the name of a rock from which a goat was thrown on Yom Kippur in ancient times.) **8.** (c) New York's Lower East Side. **9.** Lithuania. **10.** The Festival of Sukkot (or the Festival of Tabernacles). **11.** False. (The Oral Law was the name given to the Mishnah and the Gemara, and they continued to be called by this name even after they had been put in writing.) **12.** Yom Kippur. **13.** (b) the Holocaust. **14.** Flies. **15.** The law against idolatry, the law against adultery, and the law against murder. **16.** (b) barley. **17.** (d) the name of the founder of Hasidism (the Ba'al Shem Tov). **18.** (b) Casimir Funk. **19.** Taking him on as a business partner (helping him to help himself). **20.** (b) three Russian words meaning "Organization for Rehabilitation and Training."

Purim, Purim, Purim Answers

1. Hadassah. **2.** Vashti. **3.** Shushan. **4.** (c) He drew lots. **5.** Three days. **6.** Sunrise (as opposed to Yom Kippur and Tisha B'Av, which begin at sunset the night before). **7.** Haman and Mordecai. **8.** Yes (because the name of God does not appear in the Megillah, so it is obvious that an image of God has not been made). **9.** (b) in one breath (because they were all hanged together). **10.** "Lots." **11.** (b) Babylonian. **12.** A festive meal held on the day of Purim. **13.** (c) a Purim play. **14.** Hamantasch. **15.** (a) *kreplach*. (They are also three-cornered.) **16.** Two. **17.** True. (There's also the megillot of Ruth, Lamentations, the Song of Songs, and Ecclesiastes.) **18.** Iran. **19.** Haman's wife. **20.** Hamantaschen.

The World History Quiz Answers

1. (d) Theodor Herzl. (Menachem Begin was arrested in Poland for leading Jewish youths in demonstrations against Britain's restrictive immigration policy in Palestine; Haym Salomon was arrested by the British for being sympathetic to the American Revolution; Rabbi Akiva was arrested by the Romans for teaching Torah in secret.) **2.** (d) the Argentinians. **3.** (b) Ahasuerus. **4.** (c) Rashi's commentary on the Bible. **5.** Ashkenazim. **6.** Spain. **7.** (c) 1879. (It was first used by a writer in Germany.) **8.** The Jewish philosopher who lived in Alexandria a generation before the destruction of the second Temple. **9.** (a) the Greeks. **10.** (b) Albert Einstein. **11.** (b) the Romans. **12.** The Messiah. **13.** Amsterdam. **14.** Twenty-five years. **15.** Traitor. **16.** Adolf Hitler. **17.** (c) Peter Stuyvesant. **18.** (c) I. L. Peretz. **19.** (c) "Jerusalem." **20.** The airport where the hostages were being held.

1. Which of the following situations does *not* require a blessing (a *bracha*)?
   (**a**) smelling a fragrant odor;   (**b**) seeing lightning;   (**c**) seeing a giant or a dwarf;
   (**d**) smoking a cigarette.

2. According to Rabbi Meir, how many blessings should a Jew say each day?
   (**a**) 3;   (**b**) 10;   (**c**) 70;   (**d**) 100.

3. How many times is the syllable *enu* repeated in the hymn "En Kelohenu"?

4. The blessing "Blessed art Thou, Lord our God, King of the Universe, who does the workings of creation" is said on all but one of the following occasions. Which one is the exception?
   (**a**) on seeing lightning;   (**b**) on seeing high mountains;   (**c**) on seeing the ocean;
   (**d**) on seeing a sunrise.

5. What prayer is known as *benção* to Portuguese Jews and *benshn* to Ashkenazi Jews?

6. True or false: In order to conduct a religious service, you must have a rabbi.

7. How many times a year do we recite the *Ne'ilah* service?

Answers on page 108

8. Which blessing is said when a *mitzvah* is performed for the first time in the year?

9. How old is the melody of the *Kol Nidre* prayer?
   (a) 200 years old; (b) 500 years old; (c) 750 years old; (d) 1,000 years old.

10. Are the Ten Commandments included in the morning service?

11. Which is the longest of the three daily prayer services?

12. Which does not require a *minyan*?
    (a) reading from the Torah; (b) saying *Kaddish* for relatives who have died;
    (c) saying the *Shema*; (d) saying the *Borchu*.

13. Which hymn is a poetic version of Maimonides' Thirteen Articles of Faith?
    (a) "En Kelohenu"; (b) "Adon Olam"; (c) "Yigdal"; (d) "Adir Hu."

14. It is customary to recite the *Mah Tovu* upon entering a _____.
    (a) synagogue; (b) *sukkah*; (c) cemetery; (d) schoolroom.

15. Which prayer is called the "Adoration" by Reform Jews?
    (a) *Birkat Ha-Mazon*; (b) the *Aleinu*; (c) the *Amidah*; (d) the *Kaddish*.

16. When does a father say the blessing "Blessed be Thou our God who has relieved me of the responsibility for this child"?

17. Which hymn is translated as "Rock of Ages"?
    (**a**) "Adon Olam";   (**b**)"En Kelohenu";   (**c**) "Maoz Tsur";   (**d**) "Yigdal."

18. On weekdays, the traditional *Amidah* has nineteen benedictions. How many benedictions does the traditional Shabbat *Amidah* have?

19. If wine suitable for *kiddush* is not available or if one may not drink wine, it is permissible to say kiddush over _____.
    (**a**) gefilte fish;   (**b**) challah;   (**c**) the Shabbat candles.

20. Someone sleeps until 3:00 P.M. When he finally awakens, should he recite the *Shacharit* (morning) service?

1. True or false: Israeli army food is kosher.

2. Which one does not belong?
   (a) Ⓤ;   (b) Ⓚ;   (c) K;   (d) Ⓡ.

3. True or false: The Jerusalem artichoke has nothing to do with Jerusalem.

4. Abraham Levis opened the first American hotdog stand in Philadelphia in 1895. Levis invented something that goes with hotdogs. What was his invention?

5. What is the traditional topping for a bowl of borscht?

6. Which of the following birds is not *treif*?
   (a) pelican;   (b) stork;   (c) cuckoo;   (d) partridge.

7. Why does matzah have rows of little holes?

8. The first kosher butcher shop in North America was located on a famous street in New Amsterdam (later New York) in 1660. Which street?
   (a) Hester Street;   (b) Wall Street;   (c) Broadway;   (d) Fifth Avenue.

9. Are ostrich eggs kosher?

Answers on page 108

10. What is a "Hillel sandwich"?

11. The first pizza was made by the Romans 2,000 years ago using a Jewish food as the crust. What did they use for the crust?

12. How did Sir Moses Montefiore ensure that the food served to him during his travels was kosher?
   (a) He prepared it himself;   (b) He ate vegetarian;   (c) He brought along his own personal *shochet*.

13. True or false: Locusts, crickets, and grasshoppers are kosher.

14. If you took ground chickpeas, sesame sauce, and salad and put them into a pita, what would you have?

15. The name *cholent* comes from _____ .
   (a) a German word meaning "meat";   (b) a Yiddish word meaning "stew";   (c) a French word meaning "warm";   (d) a Polish word meaning "Sabbath."

16. The Grace After Meals (*Birkat Ha-Mazon*) is recited after all meals at which _____ has been eaten.
   (a) meat;   (b) bread;   (c) dessert;   (d) gefilte fish.

17. What is known as *lechem oni*, "the bread of affliction"?

18. True or false: All margarine is *pareve*.

19. What are *knaidlach*?

20. Is capon *milchik*, *fleishik*, *pareve*, or *treif*?

1. Israel is located between which two continents?

2. Who gave Eretz Yisrael the name *Palestine*?
   (**a**) the Israelites;   (**b**) the Philistines;   (**c**) the Romans;   (**d**) the British.

3. Which one of the following Israeli cities is the largest?
   (**a**) Jerusalem;   (**b**) Tel Aviv–Jaffa;   (**c**) Haifa.

4. About how long does it take to cross the State of Israel from west to east, traveling by car (Mediterranean coast to Jordan valley)?
   (**a**) seven hours;   (**b**) five hours;   (**c**) one and a half hours;   (**d**) twenty minutes.

5. True or false: The majority of Israeli Jews were born in Israel.

6. In general, do Arabs serve in the Israeli army?

7. When Menachem Begin was in the Irgun, the underground movement that fought for Palestine's independence against the British Mandatory government, he often was disguised as _____.
   (**a**) an old woman;   (**b**) an Arab;   (**c**) a bearded rabbi;   (**d**) a camel.

Answers on page 108

8. Theodor Herzl suggested a different Zionist flag from the one now used by the State of Israel. What did Herzl's suggested flag look like?

(**a**) a gold *Magen David* on a red background;   (**b**) a white flag with a blue menorah in the center;   (**c**) seven blue stripes with six white stars;   (**d**) seven gold stars against a white background.

9. Which city in Israel is not mentioned in the Bible?

(**a**) Hebron;   (**b**) Beersheba;   (**c**) Tel Aviv;   (**d**) Jerusalem.

10. When did Moshe Dayan lose his eye?

(**a**) 1941;   (**b**) 1948;   (**c**) 1956;   (**d**) 1967.

11. Has a Miss Israel ever won the Miss Universe pageant?

12. Which city in Israel is named after philanthropist Nathan Straus?

13. Israel has not one, but two, chief rabbis. Which two communities do they represent?

14. The giant menorah that stands outside the Knesset building in Jerusalem was a gift to the people of Israel from the parliament of which country?

15. Approximately what percentage of Israel's population lives on *kibbutzim* today?
    (**a**) 48.2 per cent;   (**b**) 23.9 per cent;   (**c**) 12.5 per cent;   (**d**) 2.7 per cent.

16. Kibbutz Yad Mordecai in Israel is named after _____ .
    (**a**) Mordecai of the Purim story;   (**b**) Mordecai Anilewicz, leader of the Warsaw Ghetto Uprising;   (**c**) Mordecai Kaplan, founder of Reconstructionism.

17. Which building in Israel houses the famous "Chagall windows"?

18. What picture was on the first stamps issued by the State of Israel on May 16, 1948?
    (**a**) a *Magen David*;   (**b**) a portrait of Theodor Herzl;   (**c**) ancient Jewish coins;
    (**d**) a menorah.

19. Which of the following people was born in Israel?
    (**a**) Menachem Begin, former Israeli prime minister;   (**b**) David Ben-Gurion, first prime minister of Israel;   (**c**) Gene Simmons, bass guitarist of the rock group Kiss.

20. *Mapai, Likud,* and *Mapam* are names of Israeli _____ .

Answers

Prayers, Hymns, and Blessings Answers

1. (**d**) smoking a cigarette. **2.** (**d**) 100. **3.** Twenty. **4.** (**c**) on seeing the ocean. (On this occasion one says, "Blessed art Thou, Lord our God, King of the Universe, who has made the great sea.") **5.** *Birkat Ha-Mazon* (the "Grace After Meals"). **6.** False. **7.** Once (during the closing minutes of Yom Kippur). **8.** The *Shehecheyanu.* **9.** (**d**) 1,000 years old. **10.** No. **11.** *Shacharit* (the morning service). **12.** (**c**) saying the *Shema.* **13.** (**c**) "Yigdal." **14.** (**a**) synagogue. **15.** (**b**) the *Aleinu.* **16.** At his child's bar or bat mitzvah. **17.** (**c**) "Maoz Tsur." **18.** Seven. **19.** (**b**) challah. **20.** No. (The morning, afternoon, and evening services—*Shacharit, Minchah,* and *Ma'ariv*—must be said in their appropriate time slots.)

Ess, Ess, Mein Kindt Answers

1. True. **2.** (**d**) Ⓡ. (The others are symbols indicating kosher food; Ⓡ is the symbol for "registered trademark.") **3.** True. (The name is a corruption of the Italian word *girasole,* "turning to the sun," which is a name of a species of sunflower with edible roots.) **4.** The hotdog bun. **5.** Sour cream. **6.** (**d**) partridge. **7.** To keep it from curling, getting bumpy, or rising in the oven. **8.** (**b**) Wall Street. **9.** No. (Eggs from nonkosher birds are not kosher.) **10.** Bitter herbs put between two pieces of matzah, eaten at the Passover seder. **11.** Matzah. **12.** (**c**) He brought along his own personal *shochet.* **13.** True (Lev. 11:22). **14.** A felafel sandwich. **15.** (**c**) a French word meaning "warm" (*chaud*). **16.** (**b**) bread. **17.** Matzah. **18.** False. (Many brands contain milk, milk by-products, or nonfat milk.) **19.** Matzah balls. **20.** *Fleishik.*

All About Israel Answers

1. Africa and Asia. **2.** (**c**) the Romans. **3.** (**a**) Jerusalem. **4.** (**c**) one and a half hours. **5.** True. **6.** No. (There are some exceptions.) **7.** (**c**) a bearded rabbi. **8.** (**d**) seven gold stars against a white background. (The white was to signify the new and pure life, the seven stars the seven-hour workday.) **9.** (**c**) Tel Aviv. **10.** (**a**) 1941. **11.** Yes. (Rina Messinger in 1976.) **12.** Netanya. **13.** Ashkenazim and Sephardim. **14.** Great Britain. **15.** (**d**) 2.7 per cent. **16.** (**b**) Mordecai Anilewicz, leader of the Warsaw Ghetto Uprising. **17.** The Hebrew University–Hadassah Medical Center. **18.** (**c**) ancient Jewish coins. **19.** Gene Simmons, bass guitarist of the rock group Kiss. **20.** Political parties.

1. Where was Golda Meir born?

2. Which country has more Jews, Argentina or Brazil?

3. Which of the following U.S. towns was *not* named for a Jew?
   (**a**) Aaronsburg, Pennsylvania;   (**b**) Heppner, Oregon;   (**c**) Fairfield, New Jersey;
   (**d**) Castroville, Texas.

4. What direction do Jews in India and China face while praying?

5. "The Red Sea" is actually an incorrect translation of the name of the body of water crossed by Moses and the Israelites. What is its correct English name?

6. True or false: It never snows in Jerusalem.

7. Where was the Talmud first printed?
   (**a**) Jerusalem;   (**b**) New York;   (**c**) Cracow;   (**d**) Venice.

8. Which U.S. city has the second largest Jewish population?

9. Israel is approximately the size of the state of _____.
   (**a**) Rhode Island;   (**b**) New Jersey;   (**c**) North Dakota;   (**d**) Texas.

Answers on page 118

10. In what city do you find the Arch of Titus, built to commemorate the conquest of Jerusalem and destruction of the Temple?

11. The Bible prohibits Jews from settling in which country?

12. Which building was designed by architect Frank Lloyd Wright?
(a) the main office building of The Jewish Publication Society; (b) Beth Sholom synagogue in Elkins Park, Pennsylvania; (c) the Student Center building of Brandeis University; (d) the Yad Vashem Holocaust memorial.

13. Which two cities appear together in many Jewish stories because of their silly, similar-sounding names?
(a) Minsk and Pinsk; (b) Moscow and Cracow; (c) Lublin and Dublin.

14. Hester, Essex, Ludlow, Norfolk, and Bayard are all names of streets _____.
(a) on New York's Lower East Side; (b) on Miami Beach's Hotel Row; (c) in London's Jewish Quarter.

15. On which mountain in Israel is Theodor Herzl buried?

16. Outside the Knesset building in Jerusalem there is a giant menorah. How many branches does it have?

17. How many gates are there in the wall surrounding the Old City of Jerusalem?

18. All but one of the following countries have fewer than 500 Jews. Which one is the exception?
   (a) China;   (b) Haiti;   (c) Peru;   (d) Kenya.

19. Which U.S. state has the fewest number of Jews?

20. Camp David is _____.
   (a) a Jewish summer camp run by the Conservative movement;   (b) the place in Maryland where Israel and Egypt signed a peace treaty in 1979;   (c) the biblical place where David camped while fleeing from King Saul;   (d) a training camp for the Israeli army located in the Negev.

1. What article of clothing did Moses remove when he approached the burning bush?

2. Which enemy of the Jews was said to have worn a three-cornered hat?

3. In Great Britain, the father of a bar mitzvah boy often wears a _____.
   (a) gold *yarmulke*;   (b) top hat;   (c) white armband;   (d) name tag.

4. In order to distinguish themselves from the non-Jewish population, some Hasidim do not wear _____.
   (a) socks;   (b) ties;   (c) belts;   (d) watches.

5. What is the name of the Jewish man who designed blue jeans for California gold miners in 1850?

6. On which Jewish holiday is it customary to get dressed up in costumes?

7. What kind of hat is a *kovah tembel*?

8. Does the Bible mention the custom of wearing a *yarmulke*?

9. True or false: A Torah scribe wears his *tallit* and *tefillin* to work.

Answers on page 118

10. Jews are prohibited from wearing clothes made of *shatnez* material, which is a mixture of which two types of cloth?

11. A Jew says the *Shehecheyanu* blessing when he wears new clothes. But does he say this blessing when he wears new leather shoes?

12. How many pieces of clothing did the High Priest wear?
(**a**) one;   (**b**) three;   (**c**) five;   (**d**) eight.

13. Which one of the following leaders did *not* require Jews to wear some sort of identifying mark on their clothing?
(**a**) Adolf Hitler;   (**b**) Pope Paul IV;   (**c**) Alexander the Great.

14. Who negotiated the settlement of the cloakmakers' strike, also known as "The Great Revolt," in 1910?
(**a**) President William Howard Taft;   (**b**) Isaac Mayer Wise;   (**c**) Louis D. Brandeis;   (**d**) Ernestine Rose.

15. Is the *tzitzit* worn over or under the undershirt?

16. How many threads make up each of the ritual fringes in the *tzitzit*?

17. Which ritual garment is called *sargenes* in some communities?
   (a) *yarmulke*;   (b) *tallit*;   (c) *kittel*;   (d) *tallit katan*.

18. What Hebrew expression is used when someone wears a new garment?

19. On which one of the following occasions is a *kittel not* worn?
   (a) by a groom at a wedding;   (b) by a dead person when he is buried;   (c) on Yom Kippur;   (d) on Purim.

20. Is a *tallit* kosher if it has five fringes instead of four?

Wear It Well

114

1. How many times is Moses' name mentioned in the traditional Hagaddah?

2. What is the name given to special matzah made from wheat that is guarded from the time of harvesting?

3. How many days of Passover are celebrated in Israel?

4. According to Jewish folk custom, a piece of something served at the seder, if saved throughout the year, will bring good luck. Which is the lucky ceremonial food?
   (a) parsley; (b) bitter herb; (c) *afikoman*; (d) *charoset*.

5. Which of the following is *not* associated with Passover?
   (a) the Four Species; (b) the Four Questions; (c) the Four Cups; (d) the Four Sons.

6. During Passover, the Israeli government "sells" all the *chametz* that it owns (stored in army depots, warehouses, etc.). To whom is the "official" Israeli *chametz* sold?
   (a) the president of the United States; (b) an Arab; (c) the pope.

7. Which part of the seder is known as *maggid*?
   (a) dividing the matzah; (b) eating the festival meal; (c) washing the hands;
   (d) telling the Passover story.

Answers on page 118

8. Which one of the following is *not* counted as one of the Four Questions?
   (**a**) Why is this night different from all other nights?   (**b**) Why do we eat matzah?
   (**c**) Why do we eat bitter herbs?   (**d**) Why do we dip the herbs twice?   (**e**) Why
   do we recline?

9. What is the significance of the roasted egg on the seder plate?

10. When the ten plagues are recited at the seder, each person at the table
    _____.
    (**a**) drinks wine;   (**b**) spills wine;   (**c**) dips parsley in salt water;   (**d**) hits his or
    her plate with a spoon.

11. When was the matzah-baking machine invented?
    (**a**) the 1800s;   (**b**) the 1850s;   (**c**) the 1900s;   (**d**) the 1700s.

12. The "Matzah of Hope" was placed on the seder table to remember which group of
    people?

13. The Israelites crossed the Red Sea on the seventh day of Passover. To commem-
    orate this, what do the Hasidim do on the seventh day of the holiday?
    (**a**) part their hair to symbolize the parting of the sea;   (**b**) pour water on the floor
    and dance;   (**c**) jump rope to symbolize the crossing of the sea.

14. Only *one* of the following foods eaten at the seder is mentioned in the Bible. Which one?

   (a) matzah; (b) *charoset*; (c) parsley.

15. On the day before Passover one must not eat _____.

   (a) *chametz*; (b) matzah; (c) either *chametz* or matzah.

16. What is the symbolic meaning of *charoset*?

   (a) the springtime; (b) mortar; (c) tears.

17. Which of the following is *not* used in the search for *chametz*?

   (a) a candle; (b) salt; (c) a wooden spoon; (d) a feather.

18. Which pre-Passover ritual is known as *biur chametz*?

   (a) selling *chametz* to a non-Jew; (b) burning *chametz*; (c) renouncing all ownership of *chametz*; (d) searching for *chametz*.

19. What is *matzah-brei*?

20. How many seders are observed by Israelis?

Jewish Geography Answers

1. In Kiev, Ukraine. **2.** Argentina has 215,000 Jews; Brazil has 100,000. **3.** (c) Fairfield, New Jersey. **4.** West. **5.** The Sea of Reeds. **6.** False. **7.** (d) Venice (in the sixteenth century, by an early Christian printer). **8.** Los Angeles. **9.** (b) New Jersey. **10.** Rome. **11.** Egypt. ("The Lord has warned you, 'You must not go back that way again' " [Deut. 17:16].) **12.** (b) Beth Sholom synagogue in Elkins Park, Pennsylvania. **13.** (a) Minsk and Pinsk. **14.** (a) on New York's Lower East Side. **15.** Mount Herzl. **16.** Seven. **17.** Eight (the Jaffa Gate, the New Gate, the Damascus Gate, Herod's Gate, the Lions' Gate, the Golden Gate, the Dung Gate, and the Zion Gate). **18.** (c) Peru—5,200. (China has 30, Haiti has 150, and Kenya has 450.) **19.** South Dakota (350 Jews in a total population of 696,000). **20.** (b) the place in Maryland where Israel and Egypt signed a peace treaty in 1979.

Wear It Well Answers

1. His shoes. **2.** Haman. **3.** (b) top hat. **4.** (b) ties. **5.** Levi Strauss. **6.** Purim. **7.** A *"kibbutz* hat." **8.** No. **9.** True. **10.** Wool and linen. **11.** No. (Leather represents the taking of a life; therefore, the *Shehecheyanu* blessing would not be appropriate.) **12.** (d) eight. **13.** (c) Alexander the Great. **14.** (c) Louis D. Brandeis. **15.** Over the undershirt. **16.** Eight. **17.** (c) *kittel* (because it was made of a material called *serge* or *sericum*). **18.** *Titchaddesh* (literally, "May you wear it out and replace it with a new one.") **19.** (d) on Purim. **20.** No. ("You may not add thereto . . . nor diminish from it" [Deut. 13:1].)

Passover, Matzah, Passover Answers

1. None. **2.** *Shmurah* matzah. **3.** Seven. **4.** (c) *afikoman.* **5.** (a) the Four Species. (This refers to the four types of plants that are waved on Sukkot.) **6.** (b) an Arab. **7.** (d) telling the Passover story. **8.** (a) Why is this night different from all other nights? **9.** It's a symbol of the festival offering in Temple times. **10.** (b) spills wine. **11.** (b) the 1850s. **12.** Soviet Jews. **13.** (b) pour water on the floor and dance. **14.** (a) matzah. **15.** (c) either *chametz* or matzah. **16.** (b) mortar. **17.** (b) salt. **18.** (b) burning *chametz.* **19.** Fried matzah (pieces of matzah dipped in egg and fried on a skillet). **20.** One (but tourists from the Diaspora are given an opportunity to celebrate a second seder at public functions).

1. How many Jews came to America on the *Mayflower*?

2. How many of the fifty states contain one or more places (towns, counties, mountains, lakes, etc.) named after Jews?
   (**a**) fifty; (**b**) thirty-five; (**c**) twenty-five; (**d**) fifteen.

3. In what city was the first Jewish community in North America located?

4. Approximately how many Jews were living in the American colonies in 1775?
   (**a**) 5,000; (**b**) 2,500; (**c**) 1,000; (**d**) 750.

5. Abraham Mordecai, a Jew and the first white settler in Montgomery County, Alabama, built a coffin for himself. What did he use it for during his lifetime?
   (**a**) an ironing board; (**b**) a sled; (**c**) a dining table; (**d**) a surfboard.

6. In 1776 Benjamin Franklin, Thomas Jefferson, and John Adams wanted to have a Bible scene on the Great Seal of the United States. Which scene did they recommend?
   (**a**) Moses receiving the Ten Commandments at Mount Sinai; (**b**) the burning bush; (**c**) Moses leading the Israelites through the Red Sea; (**d**) Noah's ark.

7. Henry Wadsworth Longfellow wrote a poem about the Jewish cemetery in which city?

Answers on page 132

8. Captain Uriah P. Levy, who served in the War of 1812, was instrumental in abolishing what form of punishment used by the navy?

9. Mordecai Manuel Noah, American journalist, lawyer, editor, playwright, and politician in the 1800s, wanted to establish a Jewish settlement as a response to European anti-Semitism. What did he name the proposed settlement?
    (a) Zion;   (b) Judah;   (c) Ararat;   (d) Eden.

10. What is the oldest rabbinical school in the United States?

11. Hannah Adams, the first professional woman writer in America, was a Christian who wrote about the Jewish people. In 1812 she published _____.
    (a) a kosher cookbook;   (b) a book of Bible stories;   (c) a biography of ten rabbis;
    (d) a history of the Jews.

12. Where was the first Gimbels department store, opened in 1842 by Adam Gimbel?

13. The earliest known English-language Jewish newspaper in the United States, launched in 1823, was called _____.
    (a) the *Forward*;   (b) the *Jewish Exponent*;   (c) the *Jew*;   (d) the *Jewish Times*.

14. Which Jewish woman wrote the famous poem beginning "Give me your tired, your poor" that is inscribed on the Statue of Liberty in New York Harbor?

15. In the lobby of the Capitol building in Washington, D.C., there is a plaque with a picture of _____ .

   (a) Haym Salomon;   **(b)** Henry Kissinger;   **(c)** Moses Maimonides;   **(d)** Abraham.

16. Which American statesman graduated from Harvard Law School with the highest grades ever recorded?

17. In Sir Walter Scott's novel *Ivanhoe* the hero is captured after being injured in a tournament and is nursed back to health by a generous, lovely Jewish woman. Which American woman is said to have been the model for this character?

   (a) Rebecca Gratz;   **(b)** Henrietta Szold;   **(c)** Emma Lazarus.

18. Nathan Straus, who introduced the process of milk pasteurization to the United States, was a partner in which well-known department store chain?

19. Dr. Stephen S. Wise, Joel and Arthur Spingarn, and Dr. Henry Moskowitz were among the founders of which national organization?

20. When the Zionist movement was first launched in the United States, all these groups were opposed to it but one. Which group was pro-Zionist?

   (a) Reform Jews;   **(b)** Orthodox Jews;   **(c)** BILU;   **(d)** Jewish labor leaders.

1. What is the name of this historic mountaintop site?

2. This is Israel's major Mediterranean port. What is its name?

Answers on page 132

3. Where is this family praying?

4. Which building is located behind this giant menorah?

5. This city was founded in 1909 as a garden suburb of Jaffa. What is its name?

6. What is the name of this building?

7. This memorial to the Holocaust is called _____.

8. Who designed these stained-glass windows?

9. This is Israel's Dead Sea. Where are the lifeguards?

1. According to one Jewish folk custom, if a woman is having difficulty in childbirth, she is given something to hold in her hand. What is it?

(a) an olive; (b) a Bible; (c) the keys to the synagogue; (d) a candle.

2. A baby boy is born on Monday at 10:00 P.M. On what day of the week should the *Brit* take place?

3. True or false: It is permitted for a cobbler, a tailor, or a blacksmith to "moonlight" as a *mohel*.

4. At what occasion would a *sandek*, a *kvatter*, and a *kvatterin* be present?

5. One of the following people must be present at a *pidyon ha-ben* ceremony. Which one?

(a) a great-uncle; (b) a gentile; (c) a *kohen*; (d) a doctor.

6. What is often thrown at a bar mitzvah boy when he finishes his Torah readings?

7. When was the bat mitzvah ceremony introduced in the United States?

(a) 1900; (b) 1922; (c) 1938; (d) 1957.

Answers on page 132

8. The first girl to have a bat mitzvah ceremony in the United States was the daughter of _____.

(**a**) Mordecai Kaplan; (**b**) Solomon Schechter; (**c**) Milton Berle; (**d**) Golda Meir.

9. True or false: Sandy Koufax celebrated his bar mitzvah.

10. What is the plural of *bar mitzvah*?

11. True or false: A man can have a bar mitzvah ceremony at age fifty if he did not celebrate it at age thirteen.

12. Where in the Bible is the bar mitzvah ceremony mentioned?

13. True or false: A bar mitzvah ceremony, with the bar mitzvah being called to the Torah, can take place on a Monday.

14. Some Reform and Conservative congregations hold a confirmation ceremony for teen-age religious students. During which holiday is this ceremony held?

15. What is a *shadchan*?

16. True or false: A stepbrother and stepsister can marry one another under Jewish law.

17. At weddings of Israeli soldiers the *chuppah* is often a *tallit* held up by four _____.

   (**a**) olive branches;   (**b**) rifles;   (**c**) Israeli flags.

18. What is a *chatunah*?

19. A *seudat mitzvah* (festival meal) is held after a _____.
   (**a**) bar mitzvah;   (**b**) circumcision;   (**c**) wedding.

20. It is customary for Jews to be buried with some _____ from Eretz Yisrael.
   (**a**) olive leaves;   (**b**) soil;   (**c**) coins;   (**d**) photos.

1. According to the Mishnah, how many activities are explicitly forbidden on Shabbat?
   (a) fifty-two; (b) thirty-nine; (c) twenty-seven; (d) ten.

2. True or false: Buses do not run in Jerusalem on Saturday.

3. What is the "Sabbath of Sabbaths"?

4. "Shalom Aleichem" is sung on Friday night to welcome _____.
   (a) friends; (b) angels; (c) relatives; (d) strangers.

5. What is the proper ritual for lighting Shabbat candles?
   (a) say the blessing, light the candles, cover the eyes; (b) say the blessing while covering the eyes, then light the candles; (c) light the candles, cover the eyes, say the blessing.

6. True or false: Some founding members of the Reform movement wanted to switch Shabbat from Saturday to Sunday.

7. Which custom is older, the *oneg Shabbat* or the Havdalah service?

8. When is *motza'ei Shabbat*?

Answers on page 132

9. When parents bless their children on Shabbat eve, they pray that daughters be like Sarah, Rebecca, Rachel, and Leah. They pray that sons be like _____.

10. What is the name of the legendary river that does not flow on the Sabbath?

11. Which of the following activities is permitted on Shabbat?
    (a) tying a knot;   (b) erasing;   (c) cooking;   (d) reading.

12. True or false: In biblical times the *shofar* was sounded on Shabbat.

13. When is *Shabbat Ha-Gadol*?

14. According to an eastern European superstition, what will happen to a woman who drinks from the Havdalah cup?

15. Which of the following is *not* a part of the Havdalah service?
    (a) lighting a candle;   (b) drinking wine;   (c) reading from the Torah;
    (d) inhaling spices.

16. In the hymn "Lecha Dodi," the Sabbath is described as _____.
    (a) a bride;   (b) an angel;   (c) a dove;   (d) a white horse.

17. Complete this quote, originally said by the Hebrew poet Ahad Ha-Am: "More than Israel has kept the Sabbath _____."

18. True or false: If the eighth day after the birth of a baby boy falls on Shabbat, the *Brit* is postponed until the next day.

19. How many portions of manna were given to the Israelites on the day before Shabbat?

20. What are *zemirot*?

Shabbat Shalom

131

The All-American History Quiz Answers

1. None. **2.** (**b**) thirty-five. **3.** New York. **4.** (**c**) 1,000. (There were more than 2.5 million non-Jews.) **5.** (**c**) a dining table. **6.** (**c**) Moses leading the Israelites through the Red Sea. **7.** Newport, Rhode Island. **8.** Flogging. **9.** (**c**) Ararat. **10.** Hebrew Union College (Reform). **11.** (**d**) a history of the Jews (*History of the Jews from the Destruction of Jerusalem to the Present Time*). **12.** Indiana. **13.** (**c**) the *Jew*. **14.** Emma Lazarus (1849–1887). **15.** (**c**) Moses Maimonides. **16.** Louis D. Brandeis. **17.** (**a**) Rebecca Gratz. **18.** Macy's. **19.** The National Association for the Advancement of Colored People (NAACP). **20.** (**c**) BILU. (BILU is an abbreviation for the Hebrew phrase "House of Jacob, come and let us go.")

Where in Israel? Answers

1. Massada. **2.** Haifa. **3.** At the Western Wall, Wailing Wall, or Kotel Ha-Ma'aravi. **4.** The Knesset, Israel's parliament building. **5.** Tel Aviv. **6.** The Shrine of the Book. **7.** Yad Vashem. **8.** Marc Chagall. **9.** The salt content is so high, you can't sink in the Dead Sea, so there's no need for lifeguards.

Mazel Tov! Answers

1. (**c**) the keys to the synagogue. **2.** Tuesday. **3.** True. **4.** A *Brit*. **5.** (**c**) a *kohen*. **6.** Nuts and raisins. **7.** (**b**) 1922. **8.** (**a**) Mordecai Kaplan (founder of the Reconstructionist movement). **9.** True. **10.** *B'nai mitzvah*. **11.** True. **12.** Nowhere. **13.** True. (It can take place on any day the Torah is read at the service, including Mondays, Thursdays, and holidays.) **14.** Shavuot. **15.** A matchmaker. **16.** False. **17.** (**b**) rifles. **18.** A Jewish wedding ceremony. **19.** (**a**) bar mitzvah; (**b**) circumcision; (**c**) wedding. **20.** (**b**) soil.

Shabbat Shalom Answers

1. (**b**) thirty-nine. **2.** True. **3.** Yom Kippur. **4.** (**b**) angels. **5.** (**c**) light the candles, cover the eyes, say the blessing. **6.** True. **7.** The Havdalah service. **8.** Saturday night, after Shabbat. **9.** Ephraim and Menashe. **10.** Sambatyon. **11.** (**d**) reading. **12.** True. **13.** The Sabbath preceding Pesach. **14.** She will grow a beard. **15.** (**c**) reading from the Torah. **16.** (**a**) a bride. **17.** ". . . the Sabbath has kept Israel." **18.** False. **19.** Two. **20.** Hymns sung at the table during a Shabbat meal.

1. Morris "Moe" Berg, catcher for the Chicago White Sox and other teams during the 1920s and 1930s, was considered the best-educated man ever to play in the major leagues. How many languages did he speak?

2. How many Jewish players were on the 1941 New York Giants?

3. In 1938, Hank Greenberg hit fifty-eight home runs. His mother offered to do something special if he broke Babe Ruth's record of sixty home runs in a season. What did she offer to do?

4. In 1866, Lipman Pike became baseball's first professional player. How much was he paid?
    (a) $20 per week;   (b) $200 for the season;   (c) a share in the sale of refreshments.

5. Why did Barney Dreyfuss, owner of the Pittsburgh Pirates, refuse to allow Hazen "Kiki" Cuyler, his star outfielder, to play in the 1927 World Series?

6. Where did Arnold Barry "Shoulders" Latman, pitcher for the White Sox, Indians, and Dodgers in the 1950s and 1960s, go on his honeymoon?
    (a) Miami;   (b) Grossingers;   (c) Israel.

7. Name the three Jews in the Baseball Hall of Fame.

Answers on page 139

8. Al Schacht was a pitcher with the Washington Senators, but his fame in baseball came from something else he did. What was it?

9. In 1903 Barney Dreyfuss ended a dispute between members of the National and American Leagues by making a lasting contribution to baseball. What was it?

10. Before William "Chick" Starr caught for the Washington Senators in 1935–1936, he was studying to be something else. What?
  (**a**) a doctor;   (**b**) an accountant;   (**c**) a rabbi.

11. Norm Sherry was a catcher for the Los Angeles Dodgers. His former roommate, another Jewish Dodger, is in the Baseball Hall of Fame. Who is he?

12. Who was the first Jewish pitcher to win twenty games in consecutive seasons?
  (**a**) Sandy Koufax;   (**b**) Erskine Mayer;   (**c**) Ken Holtzman.

13. Abe Saperstein, a scout for the Cleveland Indians, was responsible for sending Satchel Paige to the majors. But he's more famous for founding, coaching, and owning a basketball team. Which team?

14. John Kling was a catcher with the Chicago Cubs from 1900 to 1911. What was his real name?
  (**a**) John Kling;   (**b**) John Kline;   (**c**) Jacob Cohen.

15. In a game played on the day after Yom Kippur 5726, two Jews were opposing starting pitchers. Who were they?

16. When Moe Berg played catcher for the Boston Red Sox in the late 1930s, he became friendly with a Red Sox bat boy who later became president of the United States. Who was the bat boy?
   (**a**) Gerald R. Ford;   (**b**) Ronald Reagan;   (**c**) John F. Kennedy;   (**d**) Richard M. Nixon.

17. When Al Rosen became the star third baseman of the Cleveland Indians in the 1950s, he considered changing his name. Why?

18. From 1961 until he retired as manager of the Los Angeles Dodgers, Walter Alston kept a Jewish object on his desk. What was it?

19. Larry Sherry, pitcher for the Dodgers, Tigers, Astros, and Angels and brother of Norm Sherry, had to overcome what physical handicap?

20. Which Jewish pitcher won the 1980 Cy Young Award?

1. What Hebrew month has the same name as a Japanese automobile?

2. How many days are in a Hebrew (non-leap) year?

3. The formula for calculating the Hebrew year is Gregorian year plus _____.
   (a) 5,746;   (b) 1,039;   (c) 2,468;   (d) 3,760.

4. In a Hebrew leap year there are two months of Adar, called Adar I and Adar II. In a leap year during which Adar is Purim celebrated?

5. True or false: Trees celebrate the same Rosh Hashanah as people do.

6. Why can't Yom Kippur ever fall on a Friday?

7. If the first day of Rosh Hashanah is September 16, when is Yom Kippur?

8. What holiday is celebrated on the eighteenth of Iyar?

9. How many months are in a Hebrew leap year?

10. What's extra special about *Rosh Chodesh* Tishri?

Answers on page 139

11. According to Jewish tradition, what important event occurred in the year 1?

12. How often do Jews recite the blessing over the sun?
    (a) once a month;   (b) once a year;   (c) once every seven years;   (d) once every twenty-eight years.

13. Which does not belong?
    (a) seventeenth of Tammuz;   (b) ninth of Av;   (c) tenth of Tevet;   (d) twenty-fifth of Kislev.

14. If the year 5754 is a *shemitah* year, when is the next *shemitah* year?

15. In a leap year, how many days are there in Adar II?

16. Which month contains no Jewish holidays (other than Shabbat)?
    (a) Tishri;   (b) Kislev;   (c) Cheshvan;   (d) Nisan.

17. Which month comes next?
    Nisan, Iyar, Sivan, _____.

18. In the first chapter of Genesis, God says "It was good" on all the days except one. Which day?

19. Tu B'Shevat celebrates the beginning of spring in Israel. What season is it in New York when this holiday is celebrated?

20. In ancient Israel, every fiftieth year all debts were canceled, slavery was terminated, land purchased in the past fifty years was returned to the original owners, and the land was left unworked. What was the name of this special fiftieth year?

**Tishri,
Chesvan,
Kislev, . . .**

138

The Great Baseball Quiz Answers

1. Twelve, including French, Spanish, Latin, Portuguese, Italian, Russian, Yiddish, Japanese, and Greek. **2.** Four—Sid Gordon and Morrie Arnovich playing the outfield, Harry Feldman pitching, and Harry Danning catching. **3.** Make him sixty-one baseball-shaped gefilte-fish portions. She never did, because he didn't hit another home run that year. "It's just as well," Greenberg later said. "There's no way I could have eaten all that gefilte fish." **4. (a)** $20 per week. **5.** Cuyler made anti-Semitic remarks to Dreyfuss's son when the player found out that he had been fined for refusing to slide into second base. In standing by his principles, Dreyfuss cost himself any chance he may have had to win the Series. **6. (c)** Israel. **7.** Players Hank Greenberg and Sandy Koufax and clubowner Barney Dreyfuss. **8.** He was a pantomime entertainer at baseball games—"the Clown Prince of Baseball." **9.** He originated the modern World Series. **10. (c)** a rabbi. (His father was a rabbi.) **11.** Sandy Koufax. **12. (b)** Erskine Mayer. (He won twenty-one games in 1914 and 1915.) **13.** The Harlem Globetrotters. **14. (b)** John Kline. **15.** Ken Holtzman and Sandy Koufax. **16. (c)** John F. Kennedy. **17.** He wanted a name that was even more Jewish—Rosenthal or Rosenstein. He wanted to make sure that there was no mistake about what he was. **18.** A Jewish calendar, because a controversy arose in 1961 when Sandy Koufax was scheduled to pitch on Yom Kippur. **19.** He was born with club feet and was not able to walk properly without braces until the age of twelve after a series of operations. **20.** Steve Stone of the Baltimore Orioles.

Tishri, Cheshvan, Kislev, . . . Answers

1. Nis(s)an. **2.** 354. **3. (d)** 3,760. Between Rosh Hashanah, the Jewish New Year, and January 1, the Gregorian New Year, 3,761 must be added. **4.** In Adar II (so that there is still only one month between Purim and Pesach). **5.** False. (Tu B'Shevat is the Rosh Hashanah for Trees.) **6.** Because it would be impossible to prepare food for Shabbat. **7.** September 25. **8.** Lag Ba-Omer. **9.** Thirteen. **10.** It's Rosh Hashanah. **11.** The world was created. **12. (d)** once every twenty-eight years. (The date is based on calculations by Abbaye, a talmudic sage, who said that the vernal-equinox cycle begins every twenty-eight years when the sun is about 90 degrees above the eastern horizon, on the first Wednesday of the month of Nisan.) **13. (d)** twenty-fifth of Kislev. (The others are fast days; the twenty-fifth of Kislev is the first day of Chanukah.) **14.** 5761. **15.** Twenty-nine. **16. (c)** Cheshvan. **17.** Tammuz. **18.** Monday (the second day). **19.** Winter. **20.** The jubilee year.

1. Where is the world's oldest synagogue?
   (a) Prague, Czechoslovakia;   (b) Newport, Rhode Island;   (c) Jerusalem, Israel;
   (d) Toledo, Spain.

2. In some synagogues, part of one wall is left unplastered or unpainted as a reminder of _____.

3. Approximately how many synagogues are there in the United States?
   (a) 15,000;   (b) 10,550;   (c) 3,900;   (d) 2,500.

4. Where was the first U.S. Reform congregation located?

5. Which institution is older, the synagogue or the Christian church?

6. Who sits in the balcony of Orthodox synagogues?
   (a) women;   (b) *kohanim*;   (c) children;   (d) the poor.

7. Albert Einstein appeared in a synagogue fund-raising performance playing which musical instrument?

8. The caretaker of a synagogue is called a _____.
   (a) *shammash*;   (b) *gabbai*;   (c) *chazzan*;   (d) *ba'al kore*.

Answers on page 146

9. Where is Europe's biggest synagogue?
   (a) London;   (b) Moscow;   (c) Budapest;   (d) Cracow.

10. Where is the second oldest congregation in the United States located?

11. What country was known for the unusual architecture of its wooden synagogues before the Holocaust?
   (a) Germany;   (b) Austria;   (c) Poland;   (d) Belgium.

12. What do Sephardic Jews call an *esnoga*?

13. The *Shulchan Aruch* prohibits all but one of these activities in the synagogue. Which one is permitted?
   (a) gossiping;   (b) napping;   (c) singing;   (d) beautifying oneself.

14. A non-Jewish man attending a synagogue service should observe all of the following guidelines except one. Which one?
   (a) wear a *yarmulke*;   (b) wear a *tallit*;   (c) stand when the ark is open.

15. What is the Sephardic name for a *siddur*?
   (a) *tefillot*;   (b) *tevah*;   (c) *bimah*;   (d) *shul*.

16. The Touro Synagogue, the oldest synagogue building in the United States, is built entirely without _____.

(a) wood;   (b) bricks;   (c) nails;   (d) windows.

17. The *Shulchan Aruch* says that all of the following ways of entering a synagogue are forbidden but one. Which way of entering is permitted?

(a) entering with an unsheathed knife;   (b) entering to escape bad weather; (c) entering as a short cut;   (d) running.

18. According to Jewish law, can a former pagan temple be remodeled into a synagogue?

19. The Frank Synagogue is designated as a National Historic Shrine. In which U.S. city is it located?

(a) Boston, Massachusetts;   (b) Frankfort, Indiana;   (c) Philadelphia, Pennsylvania;   (d) Franklin, Wisconsin.

20. What is the Sephardic term for *aron ha-kodesh* (holy ark)?

1. Which one of the following is not the name of a rabbi?
   (a) *Radak*;   (b) *Radbaz*;   (c) *Rashbam*;   (d) *Rofeh*.

2. Elijah of Vilna, known as "the Vilna *Gaon*," was a Lithuanian talmudist who lived from 1720 to 1797. He is mentioned in *Ripley's Believe It or Not* for having had _____.

   (a) a fortune equivalent to $100 million;   (b) a photographic mind;   (c) fifty children.

3. Besides being a sage, Hillel was also a _____.
   (a) ditch digger;   (b) woodcutter;   (c) shoemaker;   (d) pearl diver.

4. Give two other names for Rabbi Moses ben Maimon.

5. Which rabbi was tortured by the Romans for being a supporter of Bar Kochba's revolt?
   (a) Hillel;   (b) Shammai;   (c) Akiva;   (d) Judah Ha-Nasi.

6. What game was condemned by Maimonides for keeping people away from the synagogue?

7. The foundation for Jewish college students sponsored by B'nai B'rith is named after which famous rabbi?

Answers on page 146

8. In which language was Maimonides' *Guide for the Perplexed* originally written?

9. Which movement was founded by Israel Ba'al Shem Tov?

10. Reb Aryeh Levin (b. 1885), the rabbi who was known as "the *tzaddik* of Jerusalem," originally intended to become _____.
   (**a**) a musician;   (**b**) a lawyer;   (**c**) a banker;   (**d**) an artist.

11. Which one of the following works was *not* written by Maimonides?
   (**a**) *Guide for the Perplexed*;   (**b**) *Mishneh Torah*;   (**c**) *Pirke Avot*;   (**d**) *Sefer Ha-Mitzvot*.

12. In Maimonides' book *On the Causes of Symptoms*, also known as *Medical Responsa*, what liquid was recommended as being beneficial in cases of leprosy?

13. Which country was the home of the great Bible commentator Rashi?

14. Rabbi Joseph Karo was the author of the code of Jewish law known as the *Shulchan Aruch*. *Shulchan Aruch* means _____.
   (**a**) "Code of Jewish Law";   (**b**) "Guide to Behavior";   (**c**) "The Set Table";   (**d**) "Sayings of the Fathers."

15. Which one of the following was written by Maimonides?
(a) the Thirteen Articles of Faith; (b) the Eighteen Benedictions; (c) the Four Questions.

16. True or false: "Rashi script" got its name because it is modeled after Rashi's handwriting.

17. When the Romans were ready to conquer Jerusalem in 70 C.E., no one was allowed to leave the city. Rabbi Jochanan ben Zakkai, however, was smuggled out by his students. How did they do it?
(a) They pretended he was dead and brought him out in a coffin; (b) They dressed him as a woman and pretended he was the emperor's maid; (c) They hid him in a barrel.

18. What was the name of the rabbi who debated with Hillel about matters of Jewish law?

19. Which rabbi was found, frozen and covered with snow, sitting outside the window of the local college of learning because he could not afford to pay the tuition?
(a) Hillel; (b) Akiva; (c) Shammai; (d) Rashi.

20. A would-be convert once asked Hillel to teach him the whole Torah while standing on one foot. What was Hillel's answer?

The Synagogue Quiz Answers

1. (**a**) Prague, Czechoslovakia (the Altneuschul, completed in 1270). **2.** The destruction of Jerusalem and the Temple. **3.** (**c**) 3,900. **4.** Charleston, South Carolina. (It was actually a "club" that met in members' homes, a group that separated in 1824 from Congregation Beth Elohim in Charleston.) **5.** The synagogue. (The institution of the synagogue is said to have begun at the time of the Babylonian exile, in 586 B.C.E.) **6.** (**a**) women. **7.** The violin. **8.** (**a**) *shammash*. **9.** (**c**) Budapest (the Dohány Synagogue, which has room for more than 3,000). **10.** Philadelphia (Congregation Mikveh Israel). **11.** (**c**) Poland. **12.** A synagogue (or *shul*). **13.** (**c**) singing. **14.** (**b**) wear a *tallit*. **15.** (**a**) *tefillot*. **16.** (**c**) nails. (Wooden pegs were used instead, possibly because no iron tool was used in building the Temple in Jerusalem.) **17.** (**d**) running. (Running is permitted when going to synagogue, but on leaving one must walk in order to indicate reluctance.) **18.** No. The building where pagan worship took place must be completely destroyed before a synagogue can be built on the site. **19.** (**c**) Philadelphia, Pennsylvania (on the grounds of the Albert Einstein Medical Center). **20.** *Hechal*.

So Many Rabbis Answers

1. (**d**) *Rofeh*. (*Rofeh* means "doctor." Radak was Rabbi David ben Joseph Kimchi; Radbaz was Rabbi David ben Zimra; Rashbam was Rabbi Samuel ben Meir.) **2.** (**b**) a photographic mind. **3.** (**b**) woodcutter. **4.** Maimonides and Rambam. **5.** (**c**) Akiva. **6.** Chess. **7.** Hillel. **8.** Arabic. **9.** Hasidism. **10.** (**c**) a banker. **11.** (**c**) *Pirke Avot*. **12.** Chicken soup. **13.** France. **14.** (**c**) "The Set Table." **15.** (**a**) the Thirteen Articles of Faith. **16.** False. "Rashi script" can be considered a sort of Hebrew italics. It was developed by printers so readers would not confuse Rashi's commentaries with the accompanying text. **17.** (**a**) They pretended he was dead and brought him out in a coffin. **18.** Shammai. **19.** (**a**) Hillel. **20.** "What is hateful to you, do not do unto your neighbor."

1. How many people went on the ark with Noah?

2. Could Noah have met Abraham?

3. In the Bible there is one reference to a birthday party. Whose birthday was it?

4. Methuselah is best known for being _____.
   (a) wise;   (b) old;   (c) red-haired;   (d) musically talented.

5. In which part of the body was Jacob injured when he wrestled with the angel?

6. Who was David's best friend?
   (a) Jesse;   (b) Solomon;   (c) Jonathan;   (d) Saul.

7. What was the name of Joshua's father?

8. Which pair of siblings were twins?
   (a) Jacob and Esau;   (b) Rachel and Leah;   (c) Isaac and Ishmael.

9. Who was first given the name *Israel*?

10. Where did Deborah sit when she judged?
    (a) on a throne;   (b) under a tree;   (c) at a table.

Answers on page 155

11. In which body of water was Moses' floating cradle hidden?

12. When Moses sent out "spies" to investigate the fertility of the Promised Land, they came back with _____.
   (**a**) an olive leaf;   (**b**) grapes;   (**c**) milk and honey;   (**d**) a golden calf.

13. How many times did Naomi repeat herself when trying to dissuade Ruth from leaving her people?

14. Who was king of Israel after David?
   (**a**) Saul;   (**b**) Samuel;   (**c**) Solomon;   (**d**) Samson.

15. Who had a dream about a ladder?

16. Absalom, son of King David, was known for his beautiful _____.
   (**a**) eyes;   (**b**) hair;   (**c**) clothes;   (**d**) wife.

17. The Renaissance artist Michelangelo depicted Moses as having horns on his head. The belief that Moses had horns comes from a mistranslation of the biblical description of Moses as he descended from Mount Sinai. What does the Bible *really* say about Moses' head?

18. Joseph interpreted the dreams of all these people but one. Whose dream did he not interpret?

    (**a**) Pharaoh;   (**b**) the chief butcher;   (**c**) the chief baker;   (**d**) the royal cupbearer.

19. Moses is often referred to as *Moshe Rabbenu* ("Moses our teacher"). Abraham is referred to as *Avraham* _____ .

    (**a**) *Avinu*;   (**b**) *Malkenu*;   (**c**) *Morenu*;   (**d**) *Moshienu*.

20. Who was the first person to see a rainbow?

1. During which holiday season does the Manischewitz Wine Co. sell most of its wine?

   (**a**) Passover;   (**b**) Christmas;   (**c**) Rosh Hashanah.

2. Which holiday celebrates the birthday of the world?

3. Which Jewish holiday was a model for the Pilgrim Thanksgiving?

4. Which Jewish holiday occurs once a week?

5. Which holiday commemorates the victory of the Hasmoneans over the armies of Antiochus IV?

6. On which two holidays do Jews customarily give gifts to one another?

7. *Pentecost* is the Greek name for which holiday?

8. On which holiday are small boys who have not yet become bar mitzvah called up to the *bimah* for an *aliyah*?

9. The *adloyada* is the name of the carnival held in Israel on which holiday?

10. On which holiday is the Book of Jonah read?

Answers on page 155

11. Which of the following holidays is *not* mentioned in the Five Books of Moses?
   (**a**) Rosh Hashanah;   (**b**) Shavuot;   (**c**) Purim;   (**d**) Yom Kippur.

12. On which holiday are the *arbah minim* waved?

13. The story of Hannah and her seven sons, who were killed because they refused to bow down to the king, is associated with which holiday?

14. On which holiday are *Malchuyot*, *Zichronot*, and *Shofarot* prayers included in the services?

15. Which holiday takes place after the forty-ninth day of the *Omer* count?

16. On which holiday are *hoshanot* (prayers for deliverance) chanted?

17. Which holiday is also known as the Festival of the First Fruits?

18. On which holiday is a relay race held in Israel, beginning in the city of Modin?

19. On which holiday are Israeli jelly doughnuts, called *sufganiyot*, traditionally eaten?

20. On which holiday are the *Chatan Torah* and *Chatan Bereshit* called to the Torah?

1. What was Chaim Weizmann's English first name?
   (a) Charles;   (b) Carl;   (c) Christopher;   (d) Hiram.

2. Which kosher wine manufacturer, with its headquarters on the Lower East Side in New York, had as its slogan "The Wine You Can Almost Cut with a Knife"?
   (a) Manischewitz;   (b) Carmel;   (c) Schapiro's;   (d) Mogen David.

3. The annual membership fee of the Zionist Organization is known as the _____.
   (a) *shekel*;   (b) *gelt*;   (c) *pushke*;   (d) *dinero*.

4. What shape was the Holy of Holies?

5. Jews use the abbreviations "B.C.E." and "C.E." in place of _____.

6. Which of the following is *not* a Jewish organization?
   (a) ORT;   (b) BBYO;   (c) USY;   (d) GPO.

7. Which city has more Jews—Dallas, Texas, or St. Louis, Missouri?

8. *Shtchav* is _____.
   (a) soup;   (b) chicken fat;   (c) pastry.

Answers on page 155

9. What happens in Chapter 10 of the Book of Ruth?

10. Whom did Dr. Jonas Salk use as the first human guinea pigs for his polio vaccine when it was in the experimental stage?
(**a**) prisoners; (**b**) himself and his children; (**c**) Franklin D. Rooosevelt and his family; (**d**) Israeli soliders.

11. What was Hannah Szenes's job in the Haganah?

12. How many times is the term *Judaism* mentioned in the Bible?

13. Which part of the seder comes next?
washing the hands, eating the vegetable dipped in salt water, dividing the matzah, _____.
(**a**) eating the bitter herb; (**b**) telling the Passover story; (**c**) the festival meal; (**d**) blessing the wine.

14. The word *yeshiva* comes from the Hebrew root meaning _____.
(**a**) "to sit"; (**b**) "to study"; (**c**) "to learn"; (**d**) "to pray."

15. The word *longhairs*, used to describe brainy people, was inspired by which famous Jew?

16. From what language does the name of the *hora* dance come?
    (**a**) Hebrew; (**b**) Yiddish; (**c**) Romanian; (**d**) Russian.

17. Which one of the following groups is *not* considered Sephardim?
    (**a**) Spanish Jews; (**b**) Portuguese Jews; (**c**) Italian Jews; (**d**) Middle Eastern Jews.

18. What is the largest Jewish women's organization in the world?

19. Yitzhak Navon, who later became president of Israel, was David Ben-Gurion's teacher. What subject did Navon teach?
    (**a**) Spanish; (**b**) driver education; (**c**) tennis; (**d**) computer science.

20. The word *psalm* comes from the word *psalmos*, which means _____.
    (**a**) "poem"; (**b**) "prayer"; (**c**) "song"; (**d**) "the music of stringed instruments."

Heroes and Heroines Answers

1. Seven. **2.** Yes. When Noah died, Abraham was sixty years old. **3.** Pharaoh's. ("And it came to pass the third day, which was Pharaoh's birthday, that he made a feast unto all his servants" [Gen. 40:20].) **4. (b)** old. **5.** His hip socket was wrenched at the thigh muscle. **6. (c)** Jonathan (the son of David's adversary King Saul; Jonathan, a brave soldier, died fighting the Philistines on Mount Gilboa). **7.** Nun. **8. (a)** Jacob and Esau. **9.** Jacob. (On the way back to his homeland after having spent twenty-one years in hiding from his brother Esau, Jacob met a mysterious stranger and wrestled with him. Since the stranger was really God's messenger, Jacob was given the name *Yisrael* ["he who fights God"].) **10. (b)** under a tree. **11.** The Nile. **12. (b)** grapes. **13.** Three times. (Therefore, the rabbis ruled that one must attempt to dissuade a would-be convert three times.) **14. (c)** Solomon. **15.** Jacob. **16. (b)** hair. **17.** He had rays of light shining from his head. (The Hebrew word *koran* ["shone"] was incorrectly translated as *keren* ["horn"].) **18. (b)** the chief butcher. **19. (a)** *Avinu* ("Abraham our father"). **20.** Noah.

Holidays, Holidays Answers

1. (b) Christmas. **2.** Rosh Hashanah. **3.** Sukkot. **4.** Shabbat. **5.** Chanukah. **6.** Chanukah and Purim. **7.** Shavuot. **8.** Simchat Torah. **9.** Purim. **10.** Yom Kippur. **11. (c)** Purim. **12.** Sukkot. **13.** Chanukah. **14.** Rosh Hashanah. **15.** Shavuot. **16.** Sukkot. **17.** Shavuot. **18.** Chanukah. **19.** Chanukah. **20.** Simchat Torah.

Mishmash III Answers

1. (a) Charles. **2. (c)** Schapiro's. **3. (a)** *shekel*. **4.** Square. **5.** B.C. and A.D. **6. (d)** GPO (the U.S. Government Printing Office). **7.** St. Louis has 53,500 Jews; Dallas has 35,000. **8. (a)** soup. **9.** Nothing; the Book of Ruth has only four chapters. **10. (b)** himself and his children. **11.** She was a parachutist. **12.** None. **13. (b)** telling the Passover story. **14. (a)** "to sit." **15.** Albert Einstein. **16. (c)** Romanian. **17. (c)** Italian Jews. **18.** Hadassah. **19. (a)** Spanish. **20. (d)** "the music of stringed instruments."

What is the meaning of the abbreviation *tushlaba* (תושלב"ע)?

At the end of Jewish books on traditional subjects, it was customary to end with the abbreviation תושלב"ע , composed of the initials of six words that make up a phrase expressing thanks to the Author of the universe for enabling the author of the book to finish the text.

תַּם וְנִשְׁלָם, שֶׁבַח לָאֵ', בּוֹרֵא עוֹלָם.

("Done and fulfilled, thanks to God, Creator of the universe.")

Asimov, Isaac. *Animals of the Bible*. Garden City, N.Y.: Doubleday, 1978.

Ausubel, Nathan. *The Book of Jewish Knowledge*. New York: Crown, 1964.

———. *Pictorial History of the Jewish People*. New York: Crown, 1953.

Ben-Asher, Naomi, and Hayim Leaf, eds. *The Junior Jewish Encyclopedia*. New York: Shengold, 1963.

Bermant, Chaim. *The Walled Garden: The Saga of Jewish Family Life and Tradition*. New York: Macmillan, 1975.

Birnbaum, Philip. *A Book of Jewish Concepts*. New York: Hebrew Publishing Company, 1964.

Bridger, David, and Samuel Wolk, eds. *The New Jewish Encyclopedia*. New York: Behrman House, 1962.

Burstein, Chaya M. *The Jewish Kids Catalog*. Philadelphia: The Jewish Publication Society of America, 1983.

Chill, Abraham. *The Mitzvot: The Commandments and Their Rationale*. New York: Bloch, 1974.

Comay, Joan. *Who's Who in Jewish History: After the Period of the Old Testament*. New York: David McKay, 1974.

de Lange, Nicholas. *Atlas of the Jewish World*. New York: Facts on File, 1984.

Donin, Hayim Halevy, comp. *Sukkot*. Jerusalem: Keter, 1974.

———. *To Pray as a Jew*. New York: Basic, 1980.

Drucker, Malka. *Hanukkah: Eight Nights, Eight Lights*. New York: Holiday House, 1980.

———. *Rosh Hashanah and Yom Kippur: Sweet Beginnings*. New York: Holiday House, 1981.

———. *Shabbat: A Peaceful Island*. New York: Holiday House, 1983.

Eban, Abba. *Heritage: Civilization and the Jews*. New York: Summit, 1984.

Encyclopedia Judaica. Jerusalem: Keter, 1972.

Epstein, Morris. *All About Jewish Holidays and Customs*, rev. ed. New York: Ktav, 1970.

———. *A Pictorial Treasury of Jewish Holidays and Customs*. New York: Ktav, 1959.

Ganz, Yaffa. *Who Knows One? A Book of Jewish Numbers*. Jerusalem: Feldheim, 1981.

Gersh, Harry, with Eugene B. Borowitz and Hyman Chanover. *When a Jew Celebrates*. New York: Behrman House, 1971.

Goldberg, M. Hirsh. *The Jewish Connection*. New York: Bantam, 1977.

Golden, Harry. *The Greatest Jewish City in the World*. Garden City, N.Y.: Doubleday, 1972.

Goldman, Alex J. *A Handbook for the Jewish Family*. New York: Bloch, 1958.

Greenberg, Blu. *How to Run a Traditional Jewish Household*. New York: Simon & Schuster, 1983.

Gross, David C. *The Jewish People's Almanac*. Garden City, N.Y.: Doubleday, 1981.

———. *1,001 Questions and Answers About Judaism*. Garden City, N.Y.: Doubleday, 1978.

———. *Pride of Our People*. Garden City, N.Y.: Doubleday, 1979.

Hausdorff, David M. *A Book of Jewish Curiosities*. New York: Crown, 1955.

Heller, Abraham Mayer. *The Vocabulary of Jewish Life*. New York: Hebrew Publishing Company, 1967.

Kaploun, Uri, comp. *The Synagogue*. Jerusalem: Keter, 1973.

Katzman, Jacob. *Jewish Influence on Civilization*. New York: Bloch, 1974.

Kolatch, Alfred J. *The Jewish Book of Why*. Middle Village, N.Y.: Jonathan David, 1981.

Koppman, Lionel, and Bernard Postal. *Guess Who's Jewish in American History*. New York: Signet, 1978.

Landau, Ron. *The Book of Jewish Lists*. New York: Stein & Day, 1984.

Markowitz, Sidney L. *What You Should Know About Jewish Religion, History, Ethics and Culture*. New York: Citadel, 1955.

Meltzer, Milton, *The Jews in America: A Picture Album*. Philadelphia: The Jewish Publication Society, 1985.

Metter, Bert. *Bar Mitzvah, Bat Mitzvah*. New York: Ticknor & Fields, 1984.

Ministry of Information, ed. *Facts About Israel*. Jerusalem: Ministry of Information, 1975.

Novak, William, and Moshe Waldocks, eds. *The Big Book of Jewish Humor*. New York: Harper & Row, 1981.

Paterson, Moira, *et al.*, eds. *The Bar Mitzvah Book*. New York: Praeger, 1975.

Podwal, Mark. *A Jewish Bestiary*. Philadelphia: The Jewish Publication Society of America, 1984.

Polner, Murray. *American Jewish Biographies*. New York: Facts on File, 1982.

Posner, Raphael, Uri Kaploun, and Shalom Cohen, eds. *Jewish Liturgy*. Jerusalem: Keter, 1975.

Postal, Bernard, Jesse Silver, and Roy Silver. *Encyclopedia of Jews in Sports*. New York: Bloch, 1965.

Ribalow, Harold U., and Mayer Z. Ribalow. *The Jew in American Sports*, rev. ed. New York: Hippocrene, 1985.

Rosenbaum, Brenda Z. *How to Avoid the Evil Eye*. New York: St. Martin's, 1985.

Rossel, Seymour. *When a Jew Prays*. New York: Behrman House, 1973.

Rosten, Leo. *The Joys of Yiddish*. New York: McGraw-Hill, 1968.

Schauss, Hayyim. *The Jewish Festivals: From Their Beginnings to Our Own Day,* trans. Samuel Jaffe. New York: Union of American Hebrew Congregations, 1938.

Schneid, Hayyim. *Family*. Jerusalem: Keter, 1973.

Shenker, Israel. *Coat of Many Colors: Pages from Jewish Life*. Garden City, N.Y.: Doubleday, 1985.

Shul, Yuri. *An Album of the Jews in America*. New York: Franklin Watts, 1972.

Siegel, Richard, and Carl Rheins, eds. *The Jewish Almanac*. New York: Bantam, 1980.

Siegel, Richard, and Michael Strassfeld, *The Jewish Calendar 5745*. New York: Universe, 1984.

Siegel, Richard, Michael Strassfeld, and Sharon Strassfeld, eds. *The (First) Jewish Catalog*. Philadelphia: The Jewish Publication Society of America, 1973.

Slater, Robert. *Great Jews in Sports*. Middle Village, N.Y.: Jonathan David, 1983.

Strassfeld, Michael. *The Jewish Holidays: A Guide and Commentary*. New York: Harper & Row, 1985.

Strassfeld, Sharon, and Kathy Green. *The Jewish Family Book*. New York: Bantam, 1981.

Strassfeld, Sharon, and Michael Strassfeld, eds. *The Second Jewish Catalog: Sources and Resources*. Philadelphia: The Jewish Publication Society of America, 1976.

Tillem, Ivan L., ed. *The Jewish Directory and Almanac*. New York: Pacific, 1984.

Trepp, Leo. *The Complete Book of Jewish Observance*. New York: Behrman House/Summit, 1980.

PHOTO CREDITS Page 22 *Top* from *The Life and Work of Sigmund Freud* by Ernest Jones, edited and abridged by Lionel Trilling and Steven Marcus. ©1961 by Basic Books, Inc., Publishers. Abridged from *The Life and Work of Sigmund Freud*, 3 volumes. ©1953, 1955, 1957 by Ernest Jones. Reprinted by permission of the publisher. *Bottom* Courtesy of Chaim Potok. Page 23 *Top* Courtesy of Sandy Koufax. *Bottom* Courtesy of Jalni Publications, Inc. Page 24 *Top* Courtesy of Hadassah Picture/Slide Archives. *Bottom* Photo by Albert Kuhli, used by permission of the State Historical Society of Wisconsin. Page 25 *Top* Used by permission of The Hebrew University of Jerusalem. *Bottom* Courtesy Zionist Archives and Library, New York. Page 26 *Top* Courtesy of Joan Rivers. *Bottom* Courtesy of Isaac Bashevis Singer. Page 27 Courtesy of Susan Marx, Trustee of the Rights of Harpo Marx. Pages 73 and 74 All photos by David A. Adler. Page 75 *Top* photos by David A. Adler; bottom photo by Linda R. Turner. Pages 122 through 125 Courtesy Israel Government Tourism Administration.

About the Author

160

BARBARA SPECTOR is a native of metropolitan Philadelphia, received a Bachelor of Arts degree in English from the University of Pennsylvania, and currently resides in Center City. She works in the field of publishing and spends her leisure time rattling off little-known facts about Judaism.